Schofield&Sims

Mental Arithmetic
Book 3 Answers

Teacher's Notes

Introduction

Mental arithmetic skills are fundamental to achievement in mathematics. The purpose of *Schofield & Sims Mental Arithmetic* is to provide differentiated practice tests in key areas of the maths curriculum, to be administered regularly. In addition, there is a clear focus on how number is communicated using both number vocabulary and non-verbal mathematical signs and processes.

The series consists of seven pupil books – all of them conforming to a standard layout. This ensures that pupils are not presented with too many variables at once. The *Mental Arithmetic 3* pupil book contains:
- 36 tests grouped into three sections – Sections 1, 2, and 3 – each containing 12 tests
- two Progress Tests, with Results Charts for recording individual pupils' Progress Test results
- four Check-up Tests, together covering number, money, time, measures and shapes.

Parts A, B and C

Each of the 36 tests that form the bulk of the book appears on a single page and is divided into three parts (A, B and C) – the specific content of the parts is as described on the back cover. The division into parts enables you to ensure that differentiation takes place: Parts A and B use pictures, symbols and simple language wherever possible so that pupils with reading difficulties will not be disadvantaged. It is suggested that one test is taken each week and that Parts A, B and C are set on separate days. Since speed with accuracy is important, a time limit of 10 minutes per part is recommended. However, you may adjust this as appropriate.

Answering the test questions

The material in each section is graded so that, before any test question is attempted, the work will usually have been covered in class. The coverage of each Section is outlined on the Contents page.

The term 'mental arithmetic' implies that *answers only* are required. For this reason, the books are presented in a one-per-pupil format, so that answers can be written in the blanks. If the pupils are allowed rough paper for workings out, remember that their responses will be slower.

> **Please note:** You should explain to the pupils that the device ■, used in Part A, indicates a missing number.

Marking

A separate book of answers, like this one, is available to accompany each pupil book. When the pupils have completed a test you may read out the answers as they mark their own work. If work has been done in small groups or individually, the pupils could refer to the answer book themselves.

Progress Tests

The Progress Tests, each consisting of 20 items, appear at the end of Sections 1 and 2. These are designed as timed tests, to take exactly 10 minutes each. Each Progress Test should be administered on four different occasions, under test conditions that are as similar as possible each time. So that the test can be reused, ask pupils to write their answers on a separate sheet of paper, rather than in the pupil book. Alternatively, you may photocopy a Progress Test page that has not been completed, and have the pupils write their answers on the copy. After each attempt at a Progress Test has been marked, record each pupil's results on the Results Chart provided, or invite pupils to do so themselves.

> **Please note:** Photocopying restrictions have been waived on the two Progress Tests and the two Results Charts that appear in the pupil book (pages 16, 17, 30 and 31). **Photocopying other pages – from the pupil book or from this book of answers – is not allowed.**

Check-up Tests

The Check-up Tests at the back of the book focus on specific topics. Administer them at the end of the school year or when a pupil finishes the book: the results will give you an insight into any areas of weakness. When the pupil moves up to a new class, the completed book should be given to the new teacher so that he or she can plan work accordingly.

Contents

Section 1　Test 1

A

		ANSWER
1	Th H T U Write in words the number shown on the abacus picture.	two thousand and fifty-four
2	$(3 \times 9) + 6$	33
3	$5 + \boxed{} = 13$	8
4	$9 \text{ cm } 4 \text{ mm} = \boxed{} \text{ mm}$	94 mm
5	$237\text{p} = £\boxed{}$	£ 2·37
6	80×10	800
7	$(18 \div 3) - (16 \div 4)$	2
8	3 TENS − 23p	7p
9	$28\text{p} + 80\text{p} = £\boxed{}$	£ 1·08
10	$£6 = \boxed{}$ FIFTIES	12 FIFTIES
11	$1 \text{ h } 50 \text{ min} = \boxed{} \text{ min}$	110 min
12	$300 - 175$	125

B

		ANSWER
1	Add four hundred to one thousand and ten. Answer in figures.	1410
2	Increase 29 by 33.	62
3	Find the change from a FIFTY after spending 28p.	22p
4	Multiply £0·40 by 8.	£ 3·20
5	Write 87 to the nearest 10.	90
6	Divide 200 by 10.	20
7	Write as £s the sum of 26p, 28p and 50p.	£ 1·04
8	$27\text{p} = \boxed{}$ FIVES plus 6 TWOS	3 FIVES
9	How many tenths in $1\frac{1}{2}$?	$\frac{15}{10}$
10	Subtract 36p from £1.	64p
11	How many TWOS have the same value as 4 TENS?	20 TWOS
12	Find the cost of one if 10 cost £1.	10p

C

		ANSWER
1	$\boxed{1 \ 2 \ 4 \ 6 \ 8 \ 9}$ Which of these numbers will not divide into 36 without a remainder?	8
2	$24 + 28 = x + 12$ Find the value of x.	40
3	How much greater is 4×7 than $4 + 7$?	17
4	This clock is 14 min slow. Write the correct time using a.m. or p.m. evening	9.07 p.m.
5	By how much is the value of 15 TWOS less than the value of 9 FIVES?	15p
6	If 100 grams of grapes cost 30p how much will 350 grams cost?	£ 1·05
7	$(54 \div 9) + (6 \times 6)$	42
8	$\boxed{0 \ 7 \ 9 \ 1}$ Arrange these figures to make the largest possible number.	9710
9	48 mm Find the diameter of each of the circles.	8 mm
10	If $\frac{1}{2}$ kg costs 86p, how much will $\frac{3}{4}$ kg cost?	£ 1·29
11	Posts on a motorway are 100 m apart. Find in km the distance between 11 of the posts.	1 km
12	W　　X　　Y　　Z Name the two rectangles each of which has three quarters shaded.	X　Y

Section 1 Test 2

A | ANSWER

1 Th H T U

Write in words the number shown on the abacus picture.

four thousand six hundred and two

2 $180 + 30$ — 210

3 $600 \div 10$ — 60

4 98 mm = ▢ cm ▢ mm — 9 cm 8 mm

5 $(8 \times 8) + 7$ — 71

6 204 cm = ▢ m ▢ cm — 2 m 4 cm

7 $240 - 70$ — 170

8 £4 = ▢ TWENTIES — 20 TWENTIES

9 $\frac{1}{5}$ of 25 + $\frac{1}{7}$ of 7 — 6

10 $22 + 8 + 34$ — 64

11 75 min = ▢ h ▢ min — 1 h 15 min

12 £1·00 − ▢ p = 53p — 47p

B | ANSWER

1 Write in figures three thousand one hundred and fourteen. — 3114

2 By how many g is 820 g less than 1 kg? — 180 g

3 Divide 1 metre by 5. Answer in cm. — 20 cm

4 Find the change from a FIFTY after spending 16p. — 34p

5 Find the cost of one if 10 cost £2. — 20 p

6 How many eighths in 5 whole ones? — $\frac{40}{8}$

7 84p = 7 TENS + ▢ TWOS — 7 TWOS

8 Find the sum of £0·24 and £0·69. — £ 0·93

9 What must be added to 75p to make £1·50? — 75p

10 How many min from 7.47 a.m. to 8.15 a.m.? — 28 min

11 One costs £0·49. Find the cost of 3. — £ 1·47

12 Find the difference between 7×9 and 9×6. — 9

C | ANSWER

1 Take two thousand and twenty from 2222. — 202

2 What number other than 1, 3 and 27 will divide into 27 without leaving a remainder? — 9

3 W X Y Z

Which of the triangles is a right-angled triangle and has two equal sides? — W

4 One quarter of a class of 32 children wear spectacles. How many children do not wear them? — 24

5 Which 3 coins are given in change from £2 after spending £1·35? — 50p 10p 5p

6 300 g $\frac{1}{2}$ kg 400 g 250 g

Write the total mass of the 4 tins in kg and g. — 1 kg 450 g

7 If Jack walks at 6 kilometres per hour, how far will he walk from 8.30 a.m. to 11.00 a.m.? — 15 km

8 Find the difference between (7×10) and (7×100). — 630

9 Mother bought a box containing 500 straws. If she uses 20 straws each week, for how many weeks will the straws last? — 25

10 Write the sum of £0·36, £1·24 and £1·40. — £ 3·00

11

class 1	class 2	class 3	class 4
25	26	25	24

How many children altogether in the 4 classes? — 100

12 If meat is sold at £2 per $\frac{1}{2}$ kg, how many grams can be bought for

(a) £1 — (a) 250 g

(b) 50p? — (b) 125 g

5

Section 1 Test 3

A

		ANSWER
1	910 + 90	1000
2	18p + 7p = 1 TWENTY + ▊ p	5p
3	15 × 10	150
4	A FIFTY − 18p	32p
5	(10 × 0) + (4 × 8)	32
6	43 + 47	90
7	400 − 120	280
8	1 kg − 250 g	750 g
9	£3 = ▊ FIVES	60 FIVES
10	1 h 45 min = ▊ min	105 min
11	£2·67 = ▊ TENS + 7p	26 TENS
12	($\frac{1}{6}$ of 42) + ($\frac{1}{5}$ of 30)	13

B

		ANSWER
1	Find the total of 29 and 81.	110
2	What is the change from a FIFTY after spending 19p and 18p?	13p
3	Decrease 20 cm by 20 mm.	18 cm
4	Multiply 6 by 7 and add 8.	50
5	Write 124 mm to the nearest cm.	12 cm
6	What sum of money is six times greater than £0·19?	£ 1·14
7	£0·68 = 1 FIFTY + ▊ TWOS	9 TWOS
8	$\frac{1}{2}$ kg costs £1·50. What is the cost of 100 g?	30p
9	How many FIVES are equal to £2·75?	55 FIVES
10	How many times greater is £4·20 than 42p?	10
11	How many days altogether in the 6th and 7th months of the year?	61 days
12	How much change from 4 TWENTIES after buying 8 buttons at 9p each?	8p

C

		ANSWER
1	Write this date in figures only. The twenty-first day of August nineteen eighty-three	21.8.1983 ('83)

2 How many more grams must be placed on pan Z to make the scales balance? Y 1½ kg Z 800 g   700 g

3	(4 × 0) + (1 × 9) + (10 × 1)	19

4
| 2 TWENTIES |
| 6 TENS |
| 9 FIVES |
| 4 TWOS |

Katie made this list of the coins she had saved. How much had she altogether?   £ 1·53

5 1 TWENTY and a FIVE were given as change from £2. How much had been spent?   £ 1·75

6 Write the missing signs +, −, ×
or ÷ in place of ● and ▲.
9 ● 4 = 25 ▲ 5

● −

▲ ÷

7 10 mm 14 mm 20 mm How much greater is the distance round the rectangle than the distance round the square?   4 mm

8 If 1 kg costs £1, find the cost of
(a) 100 g   (a) 10p
(b) 300 g.   (b) 30p

9 Add three-quarters of 24 to one-seventh of 56.   26

10 Samina was born in January but Hassan was born 5 months earlier. In what month was Hassan born?   August

11 5 biscuits of equal value cost 40p. What do 3 of the biscuits cost?   24p

12
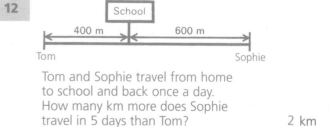

School
400 m   600 m
Tom   Sophie

Tom and Sophie travel from home to school and back once a day. How many km more does Sophie travel in 5 days than Tom?   2 km

Section 1   Test 4

A

		ANSWER
1	485 = ☐ tens + 5 units	48 TENS
2	$2\frac{1}{2}$ kg = ☐ g	2500 g
3	2000 + 900 + 70 + 6	2976
4	25 cm = ☐ mm	250 mm
5	9000 ÷ 10	900
6	£1·00 − 82p	18p
7	37 ÷ 4 = ☐ rem. ☐	9 rem. 1
8	☐p − 8p = 5p	13p
9	3103 + 97	3200
10	£2 = ☐ TWOS	100 TWOS
11	1 litre − 350 mℓ	650 mℓ
12	(9 × 9) + 8	89

B

		ANSWER
1	$\frac{1}{3}$ of a number is 8. What is the number?	24
2	Subtract £1·27 from £2.	73p
3	Multiply £2·08 by 6.	£ 12·48
4	Add 6 to the product of 7 and 7.	55
5	Find the remainder when 71 is divided by 8.	7
6	28p plus 46p plus ☐p = £1	26p
7	Add the odd numbers between 24 and 28.	52
8	Increase $12\frac{1}{2}$ cm by 25 mm.	15 cm
9	How many metres in 25 cm × 8?	2 m
10	8 badges cost 64p. What did one cost?	8p
11	How many years from 1875 to 1985?	110
12	If one costs £0·05, find the cost of 100.	£ 5·00

C

		ANSWER
1	Write the time 12 hours after 8 p.m. Use a.m. or p.m.	8 a.m.
2	A man walked steadily from 11 a.m. to 2.30 p.m. at 5 kilometres per hour. How far did he walk?	$17\frac{1}{2}$ km

3

W   X   Y   Z

(a) Which of the shapes has two pairs of parallel lines, four sides of equal length and four right angles? (a) Z

(b) Name this shape. (b) square

4	Find the change from £3 after spending £1·38 and £0·22.	£ 1·40

5 If 6 lemons cost 90p what is the cost of (a) 1 lemon (a) 15p

(b) 4 lemons? (b) 60p

6	By how many is $\frac{3}{4}$ of 20 greater than $\frac{3}{5}$ of 20?	3

7 Write the total capacity of the 3 cans in ℓ and mℓ. 1 ℓ 710 mℓ

8 In a class of 14 boys and 16 girls 3 children were absent. What fraction of the children were

(a) absent

(b) present? (a) $\frac{1}{10}$ (b) $\frac{9}{10}$

9 A boy faces North. He turns left until he faces East. Through how many right angles does he turn? 3

10	How many packets of sweets each having a mass of 250 g can be made from a $4\frac{1}{2}$-kg pack?	18

11	The distance round a triangle having equal sides is 54 cm. Write the length in mm of each side.	180 mm

12 A packet of biscuits has a mass of 188 g. Write the mass of 10 packets

(a) to the nearest 100 g (a) 1900 g

(b) to the nearest kg. (b) 2 kg

7

Section 1   Test 5

A

		ANSWER
1	A FIFTY − 13p	37p
2	500 = tens	50 tens
3	$2 - \frac{2}{3}$	$1\frac{1}{3}$
4	186 cm = m cm	1 m 86 cm
5	2200 + 800	3000
6	167 mm = cm mm	16 cm 7 mm
7	11.16 a.m. to noon = min	44 min
8	210 × 10	2100
9	15 − 6 = + 3	6
10	77p + 25p	£ 1·02
11	(5 × 9) + 16	61
12	(72 ÷ 9) + (0 ÷ 3)	8

B

		ANSWER
1	Find the sum of £1·80 and £0·18.	£ 1·98
2	Subtract 40 mm from 15 cm.	11 cm
3	Write in figures three thousand and fifty-nine.	3059
4	Write in figures the time which is $4\frac{1}{4}$ hours after midday. Use a.m. or p.m.	4.15 p.m.
5	Multiply 9 by 90.	810
6	Add £0·19 to £2·36.	£ 2·55
7	Find the difference between £5 and £3·44.	£ 1·56
8	Write in figures the number which is half of nine thousand.	4500
9	Find in cm, $\frac{3}{10}$ of a half metre.	15 cm
10	What is the product of 5 and 75?	375
11	What must be added to 13p and 16p to equal 40p?	11p
12	Find the cost of one if 10 cost £25.	£ 2·50

C

		ANSWER
1	Find the cost of $1\frac{1}{2}$ kg at 28p per kg.	42p
2	3 TENS / 14 FIVES / 8 TWOS / 4 pennies Olivia exchanged these coins for TWENTIES. How many did she get?	6 TWENTIES
3	How far will a cyclist travel in $\frac{1}{4}$ hour if he cycles at 18 kilometres per hour?	$4\frac{1}{2}$ km
4	How many months in a year have 31 days?	7
5	A man travelled 400 km in 3 days. On the first day he travelled 130 km and on the second day 228 km. How far did he travel on the third day?	42 km
6	What fraction of the circle is (a) shaded (b) unshaded?	(a) $\frac{5}{8}$ (b) $\frac{3}{8}$
7	Tape costs 12p per $\frac{1}{2}$ metre. Find the cost of 125 cm.	30p
8	By how much is 25p divided by 5 less than 25p multiplied by 8?	£ 1·95
9	Sundeep saved 55p each week for 8 weeks. How much short of £5 has he saved?	£ 0·60
10	Sophie had 45p left after spending £1·08 and £0·27. How much had she at first?	£ 1·80
11	SILVERSIDE SCHOOL / NUMBER ON ROLL BOYS 33 GIRLS 29 The children were placed in two mixed classes of equal numbers. How many children were there in each class?	31
12	Write the missing signs +, −, × or ÷ in place of ● and ▲. 9 ● 5 ▲ 6 = 8	● + ▲ −

Section 1   Test 6

A

		ANSWER
1	$8000 + \boxed{} + 40 + 8 = 8548$	500
2	5 weeks = $\boxed{}$ days	35 days
3	$420 \div 10$	42
4	£1·00 − 28p	72p
5	$1030 + 70$	1100
6	$1\ell - 450\,m\ell$	550 mℓ
7	£1·50 = $\boxed{}$ TWENTIES + 2 FIVES	7 TWENTIES
8	$6 + \boxed{} = 9 + 4$	7
9	63 cm + 38 cm = $\boxed{}$ m $\boxed{}$ cm	1 m 1 cm
10	$(7 \times 6) + (4 \times 0)$	42
11	$(\frac{1}{6}$ of 54$) + (\frac{1}{3}$ of 12$)$	13
12	$(4 \times 5) + (4 + 5)$	29

B

		ANSWER
1	Find the difference in cm between 5 m and 465 cm.	35 cm
2	How many thirds in 3 whole ones?	$\frac{9}{3}$
3	Divide £4·20 by 7.	60p
4	Subtract 60 cm from $1\frac{1}{2}$ m.	90 cm
5	Write in figures the time which is $2\frac{3}{4}$ hours after 11 a.m. Use a.m. or p.m.	1.45 p.m.
6	Find the sum of £0·48 and £1·54.	£ 2·02
7	£0·70 = 3 TENS + 3 FIVES + $\boxed{}$ p	25p
8	$18p + 18p + 18p + 18p$	72p
9	How many FIFTIES would be exchanged for £9·50?	19 FIFTIES
10	Find the cost of 10 if one costs 25p.	£ 2·50
11	Multiply £1·99 by 3.	£ 5·97
12	How many biscuits each costing 4p can be bought for £2?	50

C

		ANSWER
1	From five thousand subtract nine hundred. Write the answer in figures.	4100
2	Divide the sum of 4p, 6p, 8p and 10p into 4 equal amounts. How much is each amount?	7p
3	What number must be subtracted from 58 to leave 29?	29
4	How much will 36 cards cost?	£ 1
5	$18 + 9 - x = 10$ Find the value of x.	17
6	Find the change from £1 after buying 6 pencils at 14p each.	16p
7	How much greater is £0·72 ÷ 8 than 42p ÷ 6?	2p
8	Find the total cost of 6 tins of tomatoes and 3 tins of tuna.	£ 5·10
9	What is the mass in kg and g of (a) the 6 tins of tomatoes (b) the 3 tins of tuna?	(a) 2 kg 700 g (b) 1 kg 440 g
10	Which of the triangles is (a) a right-angled triangle (b) an acute-angled triangle (c) an obtuse-angled triangle?	(a) Z (b) Y (c) X
11	Take $\frac{1}{4}$ of 100 from $\frac{7}{10}$ of 100.	45
12	How many minutes longer is it from 9.10 a.m. to noon than from 1.30 p.m. to 4.00 p.m.?	20 min

9

Section 1 Test 7

A

		ANSWER
1	$3\frac{1}{2}$ metres = ☐ cm	350 cm
2	£1·50 + 65p = £ ☐	£ 2·15
3	1 ℓ 600 mℓ = ☐ mℓ	1600 mℓ
4	2000 + ☐ + 6 = 2036	30
5	A FIFTY − 21p	29p
6	From noon to 4.15 p.m. = ☐ h ☐ min	4 h 15 min
7	70 × 100	7000
8	(9 × 7) + (8 × 5)	103
9	4046 + 54	4100
10	17 − 8 − 4	5
11	25 TWOS = ☐ TENS	5 TENS
12	(49 ÷ 7) + (36 ÷ 6)	13

B

		ANSWER
1	Find the product of 6 and 14.	84
2	How much greater is £5 than £3·31?	£ 1·69
3	Find the total of the odd numbers between 6 and 12.	27
4	How many fifths are equal to eight tenths?	$\frac{4}{5}$
5	Multiply 12p by 7.	84p
6	Subtract 200 g from $\frac{1}{4}$ kg.	50 g
7	4 pencils cost 60p. Find the cost of 1 pencil.	15p
8	Find the difference in length between $1\frac{1}{2}$ m and 135 cm.	15 cm
9	Write 96 mm to the nearest cm.	10 cm
10	How many times smaller is 80 than 8000?	100
11	100 cost £4·00. What is the cost of one?	4p
12	Write as £s the value of 39 FIVES.	£ 1·95

C

		ANSWER
1	Ahmed has £1·56 and Katie has £1·44. If they share their money equally, how much does each have?	£ 1·50
2	A car travels at 75 km/h. How far will it travel in 4 hours?	300 km
3	Find the cost of 500 g if 200 g cost 40p.	£ 1·00
4	How many times larger than 25 is (a) two hundred and fifty (b) two thousand five hundred?	(a) 10 (b) 100
5	A concert started at 7.15 p.m. The programme lasted for $1\frac{1}{2}$ hours. There was also a 10-minute interval. At what time did the concert end?	8.55 p.m.
6	Write 4 m 45 cm as (a) cm (b) mm.	(a) 445 cm (b) 4450 mm
7	Find the change from £2 after buying $3\frac{1}{4}$ kg at 40p per kg.	70p
8	Five less than three thousand one hundred. Write the answer in figures.	3095
9		30 35 39 42	
	How much greater is the sum of the odd numbers in the box than the sum of the even numbers?	2
10	Emily has 80p pocket money. She saves $\frac{1}{5}$ and spends the remainder. How much does she (a) save (b) spend?	(a) 16p (b) 64p
11	9 trays each containing 6 cakes were bought for a party. If 9 cakes were left over, how many had been eaten?	45
12	Write all the numbers between 40 and 60 which can be divided by 7 without a remainder.	42 49 56

Section 1   Test 8

A

		ANSWER
1	$2 \times 2 \times 2$	8
2	$\boxed{\ }$ p + £1·28 = £1·50	22p
3	290 + 120	410
4	$2\frac{1}{4}$ metres = $\boxed{\ }$ cm	225 cm
5	3000 ÷ 100	30
6	10p + 10p + 5p − 14p	11p
7	110 mm = $\boxed{\ }$ cm	11 cm
8	28 FIVES = $\boxed{\ }$ TWENTIES	7 TWENTIES
9	$2\frac{3}{4}$ kg = $\boxed{\ }$ g	2750 g
10	$(7 \times 6) + (8 \times 0)$	42
11	48 hours = $\boxed{\ }$ days	2 days
12	$(\frac{1}{9}$ of 27$) - (\frac{1}{8}$ of 8$)$	2

B

		ANSWER
1	Find the change from 2 TWENTIES after spending 23p.	17p
2	Write 4750 g to the nearest kg.	5 kg
3	Find the product of 8 and 65.	520
4	How many badges costing 6p each can be bought for £3·00?	50
5	How many months in 5 years?	60
6	What must be added to £2·52 to make £5?	£ 2·48
7	A 64-cm strip is cut into eight equal pieces. Write the length in mm of one piece.	80 mm
8	Multiply 16 by 7.	112
9	Decrease $5\frac{1}{4}$ m by 50 cm. Answer in m.	$4\frac{3}{4}$ m
10	If 1 costs 9p, find the cost of 100.	£ 9·00
11	Find the difference between (136 + 66) and (10 × 20).	2
12	How many TWOS have the same value as 20 FIVES?	50 TWOS

C

		ANSWER
1	What must be added to 25 cm and 39 cm to make 1 metre?	36 cm
2	What is the number nearest to 60 which will divide by 9 without a remainder?	63

3

Find in cm

(a) the width of the rectangle   (a)   2 cm

(b) the length of the rectangle.   (b)   8 cm

		ANSWER
4	A boy cycles at a speed of 9 km per hour. At this rate, how far will he travel in $3\frac{1}{2}$ hours?	$31\frac{1}{2}$ km
5	4 sweets cost 9p. Find the cost of 20 sweets.	45p
6	The distance round the rectangle is 20 cm. If the length is 6 cm, what is the width?	4 cm

6 cm

		ANSWER
7	Find the value of n. 13 + 19 = n + 25	7
8	This clock is 12 minutes fast. What is the correct time? Use a.m. or p.m.	6.53 a.m.

morning

		ANSWER
9	Mr Brown is 34 years 5 months old and his wife is 33 years 8 months old. How many months older is Mr Brown than Mrs Brown?	9 months

10   What fraction of 1kg is each mass?

A 200 g   B 100 g   C 50 g

A $\frac{1}{5}$ kg   B $\frac{1}{10}$ kg   C $\frac{1}{20}$ kg

11	Write these fractions in order of size, the smallest first. $\frac{1}{2}, \frac{3}{10}, \frac{1}{5}$	$\frac{1}{5}$ $\frac{3}{10}$ $\frac{1}{2}$
12	Write the missing signs + , − , × or ÷ in place of ● and ▲. (5 ● 5) ▲ 5 = 20	● × ▲ −

11

Section 1　Test 9

A

		ANSWER
1	£2·40 + 70p = £	£ 3·10
2	$1\frac{3}{4}$ m = ☐ cm	175 cm
3	6p × 100 = £	£ 6·00
4	17 mm + 18 mm = ☐ cm	$3\frac{1}{2}$ cm
5	(6 × 8) − (4 × 7)	20
6	£3·00 − £2·18 = ☐ p	82p
7	59 ÷ 6 = ☐ rem.	9 rem. 5
8	A FIFTY − 12p	38p
9	4500 m = ☐ km	$4\frac{1}{2}$ km
10	$\frac{6}{8}$ = ☐ quarters	$\frac{3}{4}$
11	24 months = ☐ years	2 years
12	11.25 a.m. to 12.15 p.m. = ☐ min	50 min

B

		ANSWER
1	Subtract 8 from 103.	95
2	Write the name of the coin which has the same value as £0·10.	TEN
3	Find six tenths of 80 cm.	48 cm
4	By how many cm is 2 m greater than the sum of 80 cm and 90 cm?	30 cm
5	Add twenty-five to one thousand and eighty.	1105
6	Find the cost of one if 10 cost £5·40.	54p
7	How many sixths in $\frac{2}{3}$?	$\frac{4}{6}$
8	How many ml must be added to 270 ml to make $\frac{1}{2}$ litre?	230 ml
9	Find the total of $4\frac{3}{4}$ m and $2\frac{1}{2}$ m.	$7\frac{1}{4}$ m
10	Write 5300 g to the nearest kg.	5 kg
11	Divide the sum of 19 and 16 by 5.	7
12	How many FIFTIES can be exchanged for 75 TWOS?	3 FIFTIES

C

		ANSWER
1	Subtract (50p × 10) from (5p × 100).	0p
2	By how many mm is the line AB longer than the line CD?	10 mm
3	Tom has 29 cards and James has twice as many. How many have they altogether?	87
4	How many bottles each holding 300 ml can be filled from a can holding $1\frac{1}{2}$ l?	5
5	Write, in cm, the distance all round this regular hexagon.	15 cm
6	How much greater is $\frac{3}{4}$ of 12 than $\frac{2}{3}$ of 12?	1
7	A car travels 40 km in 30 minutes. If the car travels at the same speed, how far will it travel in 3 hours?	240 km
8	Hassan ┃ Olivia ┃ Ali The diagram shows how the children shared £5. How much did each child have?	Hassan £1·50　Olivia £2·50　Ali £1·00
9	Which 3 coins are given in change from £1 after spending 83p?	10p　5p　2p
10	If January 27th is a Wednesday, what date is the following Wednesday?	February 3rd
11	The scale shows the mass of a bag of nuts. How much will it cost if the price is 30p for 100 g?	£ 1·35
12	By how many is 15 times 100 less than 3 times 1000?	1500

Section 1   Test 10

A

		ANSWER
1	£1·00 − 14p	86p
2	15 mm × 10 = ☐ cm	15 cm
3	£1·50 + £2·60	£ 4·10
4	5450 m = ☐ km ☐ m	5 km 450 m
5	27p × 4 = £ ☐	£ 1·08
6	$\frac{1}{5}$ of £3·00 = ☐ p	60p
7	56 FIVES = ☐ TWENTIES	14 TWENTIES
8	5 days = ☐ hours	120 hours
9	(56 ÷ 7) − (9 ÷ 9)	7
10	$\frac{1}{2}\ell$ − 389 mℓ = ☐ mℓ	111 mℓ
11	1 m = ☐ mm	1000 mm
12	(9 × 6) + (10 × 5)	104

B

		ANSWER
1	Increase 57 by 35.	92
2	Half of a sum of money is 49p. What is the whole amount?	98p
3	How many 10-cm lengths are there in 5 m?	50
4	Multiply the sum of 5 and 4 by 8.	72
5	How many p in $\frac{3}{8}$ of 40p?	15p
6	7 × y = 98 Find the value of y.	14
7	Write the time $\frac{1}{2}$ h before 12.05 p.m. Use a.m. or p.m.	11.35 a.m.
8	420 minus 80 equals 300 plus ☐	40
9	What is the cost of 8 if one costs £0·19?	£ 1·52
10	Find the difference between $\frac{1}{8}$ and $\frac{3}{4}$.	$\frac{5}{8}$
11	How much short of 3 m is 265 cm?	35 cm
12	Add 3 TENS, 7 FIVES and 6 TWOS.	77p

C

		ANSWER
1	From the sum of 24 and 29 take 13.	40
2	Arrange the figures 4, 0, 2, 5, to make the largest possible even number.	5420
3	The distance round a square is 72 cm. What is the length of one side?	18 cm
4	Write the next two numbers in this series. 8, 4, 2, 1, ☐ , ☐	$\frac{1}{2}$, $\frac{1}{4}$

5

How far is it from C to B? — 240 m

6

A boy stands at point x and faces point y. In which direction is he facing? — West

7	What is the smallest number into which both 4 and 6 will divide exactly?	12
8	A school was opened in 1958. How many years will the school have been open by the year 2020?	62
9	If 1 litre costs 70p, find the cost of (a) 100 mℓ (b) 400 mℓ.	(a) 7p (b) 28p

10

| 9 TWOS |
| 3 FIVES |
| 7 TENS |

Katie had these coins. How much more is needed to make her money up to £1·20? — 17p

11 Write the missing sign +, −, × or ÷ in place of ● and ▲.
(12 ● 3) ▲ 6 = 10

● ÷
▲ +

12 Which two coins are given in change from £2 after spending 83p and 66p?

50 p   1p

13

Section 1 Test 11

A

		ANSWER
1	1 m 50 cm ÷ 10 = ▊ cm	15 cm
2	$\frac{1}{2}$ kg + 375 g = ▊ g	875 g
3	7300 ÷ 100	73
4	$\frac{7}{8}$ of £16	£ 14
5	£3·00 − £1·13	£ 1·87
6	450 km − 360 km	90 km
7	£2·47 + £1·63	£ 4·10
8	$1\frac{1}{2}$ m = ▊ mm	1500 mm
9	(7 × 8) − (5 × 6)	26
10	25 mm × 8 = ▊ cm	20 cm
11	10.24 a.m. to 12.10 p.m. = ▊ h ▊ min	1 h 46 min
12	($\frac{1}{7}$ of 42) − ($\frac{1}{9}$ of 18)	4

B

		ANSWER
1	Write the name of the coin which has the same value as £0·02 .	TWO
2	Write the next two numbers in this series. 49, 42, 35, ▊ , ▊	28, 21
3	Find the total of £2·36 and £0·99.	£ 3·35
4	$\frac{9}{10}$ of a sum of money is £45. Find the whole amount.	£ 50
5	Write in cm the length remaining when 10 cm is reduced by 55 mm.	$4\frac{1}{2}$ cm
6	How many g are there in $\frac{1}{10}$ kg?	100 g
7	What is the difference between 42 and 420?	378
8	Six cost £2·16. What is the cost of one?	36p
9	Write 250 mm as m.	$\frac{1}{4}$ m
10	Add 2 times 9 to 5 times 9.	63
11	If 5 sweets cost 30p, what will 15 cost?	90p
12	In the number 9440, how many times greater is the 4 marked x than the 4 marked y?	10

C

		ANSWER
1	In a class library there are 138 fiction books and 144 non-fiction books. How many books are there altogether?	282
2	What fraction of 1 hour is (a) 20 minutes (b) 40 minutes?	(a) $\frac{1}{3}$ h (b) $\frac{2}{3}$ h
3	8 kg 500 g is divided into 10 equal quantities. What does one of the quantities weigh?	850 g
4	PACK OF 4 for 90p How much will 20 cans cost?	£ 4·50
5	How many hours will it take a car travelling at 70 km/h to travel 280 km?	4 h
6	By how many m is the sum of 870 m and 650 m more than $1\frac{1}{2}$ km?	20 m
7	Which number when multiplied by itself equals 64?	8
8	mm 10 20 30 40 50 60 70 Y ▊ Z Write the length of a line 100 times longer than the line YZ (a) in cm (b) in m.	(a) 650 cm (b) $6\frac{1}{2}$ m
9	Lucy has three times as much as Daniel who has 45p. How much have they altogether?	£ 1·80
10	40 m 60 m 30 m 70 m This is a plan of a playground. How many times round it must the children run in order to run 1 km?	5
11	If $\frac{1}{2}$ kg costs 40p, find the cost of (a) 100 g (b) 600 g.	(a) 8p (b) 48p
12	In the number 6365, what must be added to the 6 marked y to make it equal in value to the 6 marked x?	5940

14

Section 1 Test 12

A

		ANSWER
1	5505 − 500	5005
2	100 × 21	2100
3	14 cm + 15 cm + 16 cm	45 cm
4	3 × 3 × 3	27
5	28p + 25p + 45p = £	£ 0·98
6	£10·46 = ▨ TENS + 6p	104 TENS
7	$\frac{3}{10}$ of 1 km = ▨ m	300 m
8	8 a.m. to 6 p.m. = ▨ h	10 h
9	$1\frac{1}{2}$ kg − 600 g = ▨ g	900 g
10	(5 × 7) + (10 × 8)	115
11	$\frac{3}{4}$ ℓ − 200 mℓ = ▨ mℓ	550 mℓ
12	(36 ÷ 9) + (100 ÷ 10)	14

B

		ANSWER
1	Find the sum of 73 and 48.	121
2	Write 1560 mm as m and mm.	1 m 560 mm
3	Find half of the sum of 12p and 18p.	15p
4	What is the product of 4, 5 and 6?	120
5	How many eighths are there in 7 whole ones?	$\frac{56}{8}$
6	Find the cost of 24 articles at 6p each.	£ 1·44
7	What is the remainder when 61 is divided by 9?	7
8	How many years are there from 1984 to the year 2020?	36
9	What number is 101 less than 1000?	899
10	100 cost £10·00. Find the cost of one.	10p
11	Add the numbers between 20 and 35 which can be divided exactly by 8.	56
12	Find the cost of $3\frac{1}{2}$ metres at 16p per m.	56p

C

		ANSWER
1	Divide the sum of 7, 11, 6 and 4 by 7.	4
2	How many 30-cm lengths can be cut from a 3-metre length?	10
3	Find the cost of 2 ℓ 250 mℓ if 1 ℓ costs £2.	£ 4·50
4	What must be added to 7 + 9 to equal 7 × 9?	47
5	300 pencils cost £18. Find the cost of (a) 100 pencils (b) 10 pencils.	(a) £ 6 (b) 60p
6	Through how many right angles does a boy turn when turning from East to West?	2
7	Daniel goes to bed at 7.45 p.m. and gets up at 7.45 a.m. How many hours is he in bed?	12 h
8	CHESS SET — LIST PRICE £3·60. William bought the chess set at a quarter less than the list price. How much did he pay?	£ 2·70
9	The diagram shows two children's heights. How much taller is Fatima than Amy (a) in cm (b) in mm?	(a) 17 cm (b) 170 mm
10	How many 200-mℓ bottles can be filled from a can holding 4 ℓ?	20
11	What is half of $3\frac{1}{2}$?	$1\frac{3}{4}$
12	There are 2055 people in a village. Write the number of people (a) to the nearest 10 (b) to the nearest 100 (c) to the nearest 1000.	(a) 2060 (b) 2100 (c) 2000

Next work Progress Test 1 on page 16.

Enter the result and the date on the chart.

PROGRESS TEST 1

Write the numbers 1 to 20 down the side of a sheet of paper.
Write alongside these numbers the **answers only** to the following questions.
Work as quickly as you can.
Time allowed – **10 minutes.**

1	170 + 280	450
2	($\frac{1}{5}$ of 45) − ($\frac{1}{7}$ of 63)	0
3	(8 × 8) + (6 × 6)	100
4	(450 ÷ 10) − (3500 ÷ 100)	10
5	Write in figures nine thousand and sixteen.	9016
6	The diameter of this circle is 1 cm 6 mm. What is the radius of the circle in mm?	8 mm
7	Add the numbers between 40 and 50 which can be divided by 7 without a remainder.	91
8	$\frac{3}{4}$ $\frac{2}{5}$ $\frac{5}{6}$ $\frac{3}{8}$ $\frac{5}{10}$ $\frac{25}{100}$ Which of the fractions has the same value as a half?	$\frac{5}{10}$
9	650 g $\frac{1}{4}$ kg 700 g How much more than $1\frac{1}{2}$ kg is the total mass of the three boxes?	100 g
10	Which 3 coins are given in change from £2 after spending 60p and 78p?	50p 10p 2p
11	Find the cost of one pencil if 10 pencils cost £1·10.	11p
12	How many minutes are there from 11.17 a.m. to 12.15 p.m.?	58 min
13	A boy stands facing West and turns left through 3 right angles. In which direction is he then facing?	North
14	Find the cost of 300 mℓ if $\frac{1}{2}$ ℓ costs 35p.	21p
15	If a car travels at a speed of 80 km/h, how far will it travel from 9.30 a.m. to noon?	200 km
16	RED BLUE OTHER COLOURS The diagram represents the 64 cars which passed a school in one hour. How many of the cars were blue?	24
17	What fraction in its lowest terms is 900 g of 1 kg?	$\frac{9}{10}$
18	Write to the nearest £ the sum of £3·80 and £2·69.	£6
19	Find the cost of 100 buttons if one button costs 8p.	£8·00
20	100 p 100 FIVES 50 TENS 50 TWENTIES Write as £s the total of the contents of the packets.	£21·00

PROGRESS TEST 1

You will work Progress Test 1 at **four** different times. When you first work the test
    (a) colour the first column to show the number of examples correct out of 20
    (b) enter the date.
Each time you work the test, enter the result and the date in the marked columns.

number of examples correct	1st	2nd	3rd	4th
20				
19				
18				
17				
16				
15				
14				
13				
12				
11				
10				
9				
8				
7				
6				
5				
4				
3				
2				
1				
0				
date				

Section 2 Test 1

A

		ANSWER
1	7 + 33 + 9	49
2	814 ÷ 2	407
3	(19 + 5) − (7 + 8)	9
4	$1\frac{1}{4}$ m = ☐ mm	1250 mm
5	1 minute = ☐ seconds	60 s
6	9 + 9 + 9 + 9	36
7	$\frac{3}{5}$ = ☐ tenths	$\frac{6}{10}$
8	34p × 6 = £ ☐	£ 2·04
9	From 10.14 a.m. to noon = ☐ h ☐ min	1 h 46 min
10	1 FIFTY − yp = 17p. Find the value of y in pence.	33p
11	8^2 = 50 + ☐	14
12	61 ÷ 8 = ☐ rem. ☐	7 rem. 5

B

		ANSWER
1	Write in figures nine thousand seven hundred and nine.	9709
2	There is 69p change from £2. How much has been spent?	£ 1·31
3	Write 1700 g to the nearest kg.	2 kg
4	Divide £2·94 by 6.	49 p
5	Take 6 plus 5 from the total of 8 and 17.	14
6	How many seconds in (a) $\frac{1}{2}$ min (b) $1\frac{1}{4}$ min?	(a) 30 s (b) 75 s
7	Find the sum of the odd numbers between 56 and 60.	116
8	Which 2 coins must be added to a FIVE and 3 TWOS to make 23p?	10 p 2p
9	Find the cost of $2\frac{1}{2}$ kg at 28p per kg.	70p
10	What must be added to 5 plus 80 to equal 5 multiplied by 80?	315
11	If 2 ℓ cost 48p, find the cost of $\frac{1}{4}$ ℓ.	6p
12	Find $\frac{1}{6}$ of 84.	14

C

		ANSWER
1	Write as a decimal fraction (a) the shaded part (b) the unshaded part.	(a) 0.4 (b) 0.6
2	A plane flew 2400 km at a speed of 800 km/h. How long did the journey take?	3 h
3	How many 600-mℓ bottles can be filled from 6 ℓ ?	10
4	George had £1. He spent 28p on nuts and 42p on bus fares. How much had he left?	30p
5	The perimeter of this square is 60 mm. Find the length of one side.	15 mm
6	Ahmed has 28p and his sister has 4 times as much. How much have they altogether?	£ 1·40
7	1 TWENTY 2 TENS 8 FIVES 10 TWOS Tom exchanged these coins for FIFTIES. How many FIFTIES did he get?	2 FIFTIES
8	The first day of Joshua's holiday was June 29th and he returned to school on August 3rd. For how many days was he on holiday?	35
9	Sophie $\frac{1}{3}$ | Shahid $\frac{1}{2}$ | Sam $\frac{1}{6}$	

The diagram shows how the children shared £4·20. How much did each receive?

Sophie	£ 1·40
Shahid	£ 2·10
Sam	£ 0·70

		ANSWER
10	The sum of 3 numbers is 94. Two of the numbers are 36 and 35. What is the third number?	23
11	How many weeks will it take Chen to save £5·00 if he saves 25p each week?	20
12	36 54 64 72 Which two of these numbers can be divided by both 4 and 9 without a remainder?	36 72

Section 2 Test 2

A

		ANSWER
1	25 + 5 + 16 + 4	50
2	2009 − 10	1999
3	85p × 4 = £	£ 3·40
4	900 mℓ + 870 mℓ = ☐ ℓ ☐ mℓ	1 ℓ 770 mℓ
5	$\frac{18}{3}$ = ☐ whole ones	6
6	30 − (7 × 4)	2
7	2670 m + ☐ m = 3 km	330 m
8	£2·58 ÷ 3	86p
9	(15 − 6) + (33 − 4)	38
10	180 ÷ y = 9. Find the value of y.	20
11	Find (a) $\frac{1}{8}$ of 72 (b) $\frac{7}{8}$ of 72.	(a) 9 (b) 63
12	$2^2 + 3^2$ =	13

B

		ANSWER
1	Write as a decimal fraction (a) $\frac{3}{10}$ (b) $\frac{5}{10}$.	(a) 0.3 (b) 0.5
2	How many h and min in 95 min?	1 h 35 min
3	Which 3 coins together equal 57p?	50p 5p 2p
4	Subtract 50 from 8000.	7950
5	Write 435 cm to the nearest $\frac{1}{2}$ m.	$4\frac{1}{2}$ m
6	If 10 marbles cost 32p, what will be the cost of 40 marbles?	£ 1·28
7	What is the total of seven, twenty-nine and fourteen?	50
8	1 kg costs £1·28. What is the cost of 250 g?	32p
9	9 FIVES plus 6 TWOS	57p
10	How many g must be added to 970 g to make $1\frac{1}{2}$ kg?	530 g
11	Multiply the sum of 16 and 9 by 8.	200
12	Subtract 8 from the product of 9 and 7.	55

C

		ANSWER
1	A car travels at 100 km/h. How far will it travel in 15 min?	25 km

2

Write, in 24-hour clock time, the correct time for each digital clock if

(a) Clock X is 18 min fast — (a) 09.57

(b) Clock Y is 25 min slow. — (b) 00.15

| 3 | Find the cost of $6\frac{1}{2}$ metres of ribbon at 18p per metre. | £ 1·17 |
| 4 | A tin of fruit has a mass of 450g. Find to the nearest kg, the mass of 6 tins. | 3 kg |

5

Which line is parallel to the line AB? — GH

| 6 | Jessica bought the following: carrots 45p, potatoes 65p. How much change did she get from £2? | 90p |

7

Which of the angles w, x, y, z are

(a) obtuse — (a) w y

(b) acute? — (b) x z

8	What must be added to one-sixth of 48 to equal $\frac{1}{7}$ of 63?	1
9	Find the difference between (8 + 8 + 8 + 8) and 8 times 6.	16
10	What is a half-share of the sum of 6 FIVES and 8 TWOS?	23p

11

| TOMATO PUREE 21p per tin ★ 6 tins for £1·14 | How much is saved per tin by buying 6 tins at a time? 2p |

| 12 | 50 milk straws are used on each of 5 days in a week. How many weeks will 2000 straws last? | 8 |

19

Section 2 Test 3

A

		ANSWER
1	T U tenths Write the number shown on the abacus picture as a decimal.	32.5
2	(5 × 6) + 4	34
3	80 tenths = ☐ units	8
4	$\frac{2}{3}$ = ☐ sixths	$\frac{4}{6}$
5	46 + 64	110
6	125 × 4	500
7	$\frac{3}{4}$ min = ☐ s	45 s
8	(9 + 9) − (4 + 8)	6
9	(32 ÷ 4) + (0 ÷ 8)	8
10	£8·54 ÷ 7	£ 1·22
11	$1\frac{1}{2}$ km − 560 m = ☐ m	940 m
12	£5·00 − £ ☐ = £3·46	£ 1·54

B

		ANSWER
1	Write as a decimal fraction of a cm (a) 5 mm (b) 8 mm.	(a) 0.5 cm (b) 0.8 cm
2	How many h and min from noon to quarter to four in the afternoon?	3 h 45 min
3	Write 6 m 875 mm to the nearest m.	7 m
4	Find the cost of $4\frac{1}{4}$ kg at 16p per kg.	68p
5	Multiply 6 by 6 and divide the answer by 9.	4
6	$\frac{3}{4}$ of a sum of money is 21p. Find the sum of money.	28p
7	Find the total of (16 + 9) and (5 × 5).	50
8	Find one half of four thousand five hundred. Write the answer in figures.	2250
9	Subtract the sum of 23p and 28p from £1.	49p
10	Add the even numbers between 35 and 39.	74
11	How many FIVES are equal in value to £7?	140
12	Make each of the following 10 times smaller (a) 8 (b) 131.	(a) 0.8 (b) 13.1

C

		ANSWER
1	Write the length of the line YZ (a) in cm and mm (b) in cm.	(a) 5 cm 7 mm (b) 5.7 cm
2	Find the difference between $\frac{1}{4}$ of £0·76 and $\frac{3}{4}$ of £0·76.	38p
3	How many days altogether in April, May and June?	91
4	**S A L E** ALL GOODS REDUCED BY 15p IN THE £ How much will be paid for an article which cost £3 before the sale?	£ 2·55
5	Find the sum of money which is 30p less than the sum of 7 TENS and 7 TWOS.	54p
6	$\frac{3}{4}$ $\frac{1}{3}$ $\frac{1}{5}$ $\frac{5}{8}$ $\frac{4}{6}$ Which two of the fractions when added together equal one whole one?	$\frac{1}{3}$ $\frac{4}{6}$
7	The perimeter of a square is 10 cm. Find the length of one side (a) in cm and mm (b) in cm.	(a) 2 cm 5 mm (b) 2.5 cm
8	A shopkeeper wrote 130 kg on an order form instead of 13 kg. By how many kg was the order too much?	117 kg
9	morning evening Write in figures the times shown on the clock faces. Use a.m. or p.m.	(a) 11.23 a.m. (b) 8.52 p.m.
10	In a class of 28 children, there were 4 more girls than boys. How many boys were there in the class?	12
11	Cups cost 44p each and saucers half as much. Find the total cost of 6 cups and 6 saucers.	£ 3·96
12	Emily and Lucy are twins. For their birthday they were given 3 FIFTIES and 9 TWENTIES which they shared equally. How much did each have?	£ 1·65

Section 2   Test 4

A
		ANSWER
1	7.6 cm + 4 mm = ▦ cm	8 cm
2	Write as a decimal $100 + 10 + 1 + \frac{1}{10}$	111.1
3	50p − ▦ p = 27p	23p
4	(17 − 8) + (11 − 7)	13
5	$\frac{1}{10}$ of 1 ℓ = ▦ mℓ	100 mℓ
6	10 000 + 900 + 8	10 908
7	$3\frac{3}{4}$ = ▦ quarters	$\frac{15}{4}$
8	(8 × 3) − (0 × 5)	24
9	17p × 7 = £ ▦	£ 1·19
10	Find (a) $\frac{1}{5}$ of £45	(a) £ 9
	(b) $\frac{3}{5}$ of £45.	(b) £ 27
11	44 ÷ 9 = ▦ rem.	4 rem. 8
12	15 FIVES + 3 TENS	£ 1·05

B
		ANSWER
1	Write as a decimal (a) 36 tenths (b) 104 tenths.	(a) 3.6 (b) 10.4
2	By how many is 44 greater than 19?	25
3	Write as a vulgar fraction in its lowest terms (a) 100 m of 1 km	(a) $\frac{1}{10}$ km
	(b) 700 m of 1 km	(b) $\frac{7}{10}$ km
4	Find the cost of 20 packs of sweets if 5 packs cost 77p.	£ 3·08
5	From half-past eight to twenty to ten in the morning = ▦ h ▦ min	1 h 10 min
6	From the product of 10 and 10 subtract 13.	87
7	Find five-sixths of £54.	£ 45
8	How many mℓ must be added to $4\frac{1}{4}$ ℓ to make 5 ℓ?	750 mℓ
9	Make each of the following 10 times larger. (a) 0.7 (b) 2.3	(a) 7 (b) 23
10	Multiply 61p by 9.	£ 5·49
11	Which 3 coins make up 54p?	50p 2p 2p
12	Write the missing signs +, −, × or ÷ in place of ● and ▲. 14 ● 7 = 35 ▲ 5	● − ▲ ÷

C
		ANSWER
1	Find the whole amount of money when (a) $\frac{2}{3}$ is 30p (b) $\frac{5}{8}$ is 40p.	(a) 45p (b) 64p
2	Sophie walked at a steady speed from 10 a.m. to 12.30 p.m. She covered a distance of 10 km. What was her walking speed in km/h?	4 km/h
3	The circumference of the wheel is 1.5 m. How many m will the wheel travel in (a) 10 turns (b) 100 turns?	(a) 15 m (b) 150 m
4	It takes Mrs Brown 75 minutes to get to work. At what time must she leave home to arrive at work at 8.30 a.m.?	7.15 a.m.
5	F M N W X Z In which of these letters are there two pairs of parallel lines?	W
6	(a) How many 500-mℓ bottles can be filled from 5 ℓ?	(a) 10
	(b) How many 50-mℓ bottles can be filled from 5 ℓ?	(b) 100
7	When a number is divided by 8 the answer is 6 remainder 6. What is the number?	54
8	Find the missing numbers in this series. 1.6, 1.4, 1.2, ▦, ▦	1.0, 0.8
9	Name (a) the acute-angled triangle	(a) Z
	(b) the right-angled triangle	(b) X
	(c) the obtuse-angled triangle.	(c) Y
10	Josh had £1·80 and Leah had half as much as Josh. How much had they altogether?	£ 2·70
11	Find the cost of 90 g of wool at 40p for 20 g.	£ 1·80
12	$\frac{2}{3}$ of £12 $\frac{3}{4}$ of £12 $\frac{5}{6}$ of £12 What is the value of (a) the largest of these amounts	(a) £ 10
	(b) the smallest of these amounts?	(b) £ 8

Turn back to page 16 and work for the second time Progress Test 1.

Enter the result and the date on the chart.

21

Section 2   Test 5

A

		ANSWER
1	2.9 = ▨ tenths	29 tenths
2	49 + 63	112
3	6090 ÷ 3	2030
4	$\frac{1}{2} = \frac{x}{16}$. Find x.	8
5	(8 × 5) + (3 × 7)	61
6	10 m − 5.5 m = ▨ m	4.5 m
7	84 − 57	27
8	$3\frac{3}{4}$ km + 300 m = ▨ km ▨ m	4 km 50 m
9	From 10.20 a.m. to 12.25 p.m. = ▨ h ▨ min	2 h 5 min
10	3 TWENTIES + 3 FIFTIES	£ 2·10
11	(30 ÷ 5) + (18 ÷ 6)	9
12	10 articles cost £1·50. Find the cost of one article.	15p

B

		ANSWER
1	Write 9 km 700 m to the nearest km.	10 km
2	By how many cm is 2.4 cm less than 6 cm?	3.6 cm
3	What fraction of 42 is 7?	$\frac{1}{6}$
4	What must be added to £3·66 to make £4·50?	84p
5	By how many is 25 minus 6 less than 25 plus 6?	12
6	$\begin{array}{c} x\ y \\ 37.7 \end{array}$ How many times greater is the 7 marked x than the 7 marked y?	10
7	Increase £2·46 by £1·26.	£ 3·72
8	Find the cost of 20 cm at £2·00 per m.	40p
9	Subtract $\frac{1}{2}$ of £24 from $\frac{3}{4}$ of £28.	£ 9
10	Write as a vulgar fraction in its lowest terms 900 mℓ of 1ℓ.	$\frac{9}{10}\ \ell$
11	Which 3 coins are given in change from £3 after spending £2·84?	10p 5p 1p
12	Change $\frac{8}{10}$ to hundredths.	$\frac{80}{100}$

C

		ANSWER
1	Find the difference in g between the masses shown by pointers X and Y.	800 g
2	A plane flies at a speed of 900 km/h. How far does it travel in (a) 20 min (b)10 min?	(a) 300 km (b) 150 km
3	Name two lines in the rhombus which are perpendicular to each other.	AC BD
4	After using oil from a can holding 3 ℓ 300 mℓ only $2\frac{3}{4}$ ℓ remained. How many mℓ had been used?	550 mℓ
5	Find the total cost of 4 magazines at £2·25 each and 3 comics at £1·50 each.	£ 13·50
6	£ 0·70 0·25 0·18 Find the change from £2 after paying these amounts.	87p
7	5.5 cm / 6.7 cm Find the total length of the two lines in mm.	122 mm
8	Mr Robb arrived home at 9.50 p.m. after travelling for $2\frac{1}{4}$ hours. At what time did he start his journey?	7.35 p.m.
9	10 tins of beans have a mass of 3 kg. Find the mass in g of 1 tin.	300 g
10	The bus fare to town is £1·80, and children travel half price. Find the total bus fare for 2 adults and 2 children.	£ 5·40
11	A square has a perimeter of 1 m 60 cm. Find the length of one side in cm.	40 cm
12	Lucy spent two-thirds of her savings when she bought a radio for £50. How much had she saved at first?	£ 75

22

Section 2   Test 6

A

		ANSWER
1	19.4 cm = ▢ mm	194 mm
2	(18 + 7) − (6 + 6)	13
3	(4 × 1000) + (8 × 100) + (9 × 1)	4809
4	£4·00 − £3·24	76p
5	Write 4 ℓ 500 mℓ to the nearest ℓ.	5 ℓ
6	£1·32 ÷ 6 = ▢ p	22 p
7	Write $\frac{4}{5}$ as a decimal.	0.8
8	$\frac{1}{3} = \frac{a}{12} = \frac{b}{18}$ (a) $\frac{4}{12}$ (b) $\frac{6}{18}$	
9	120 g + ▢ g = $\frac{1}{2}$ kg	380 g
10	9.3 cm + 6.8 cm	16.1 cm
11	28 + 25 + ▢ = 74	21
12	5 articles cost £1·10. 1 article costs ▢ p.	22p

B

		ANSWER
1	Multiply 4.3 by 10.	43
2	18 cm divided by 10 = ▢ cm.	1.8 cm
3	Write in 24-hour clock time (a) 8.00 a.m. (b) 8.00 p.m.	(a) 08.00 (b) 20.00
4	10 + 2999	3009
5	From £4 take the total of £1·40 and £1·65.	95p
6	3 batteries cost £2·25. Find the cost of one battery.	75p
7	How many 50-cm lengths can be cut from 18 m?	36
8	What is the cost of 3 kg 100 g if 1 kg costs £1?	£ 3·10
9	What is the difference in mℓ between 2 ℓ 700 mℓ and 2580 mℓ?	120 mℓ
10	$\frac{9}{10}$ of a sum of money is £2·70. Find the sum of money.	£ 3·00
11	By how many is 8² greater than 7²?	15
12	Share £6 equally among 8 children. How much does each child receive?	75p

C

		ANSWER
1	DERBY 21 km If a man walks at a steady speed of 6 km/h, how long will it take him to walk to Derby?	$3\frac{1}{2}$ h
2	y × 10 = 320 What is the value of y?	32
3	Amy's father gave her 28p to make her money up to £3·15. How much had Amy at first?	£ 2·87
4	In which direction must (a) Ahmed walk to reach Hassan (b) Hassan walk to reach Ahmed?	(a) SE (b) NW
5	1 m of ribbon costs £3·20. Find the cost of 1$\frac{1}{4}$ m.	£ 4·00
6	A 2p coin is 1.8 mm thick. Find the height in mm of a pile of (a) 10 TWOS (b) 100 TWOS.	(a) 18 mm (b) 180 mm
7	15 18 20 24 30 Which of these numbers can be divided by 2, 3 and 5 without a remainder?	30
8	Megan received 3 TENS, a FIVE and a TWO in change from £1. How much had she spent?	63p
9	The line AB is drawn to scale and represents a distance of 2.5 metres. What length is represented by 1 cm?	0.5 m
10	Find the difference between $\frac{4}{5}$ of £30 and $\frac{5}{6}$ of £30.	£ 1
11	The mass of three parcels is shown on the dial. If they are of equal mass, write the mass in g of one parcel.	900 g
12	A computer game can be bought for £27 cash or by 20 weekly payments each of £1·50. By how much is the total of the weekly payments greater than the cash price?	£ 3·00

Section 2   Test 7

A

		ANSWER
1	T U t h — Write as a decimal the number shown on the abacus picture	12.31
2	50 − (6 × 7)	8
3	(19 + 8) − (6 + 7)	14
4	£1·09 + 68p = £	£ 1·77
5	Find $\frac{3}{4}$ of 28 kg.	21 kg
6	1 article costs 19p. 5 articles cost ▢ p.	95p
7	33p + ▢ p = 2 TWENTIES	7p
8	$1\frac{1}{4}$ kg − 700 g = ▢ g	550 g
9	£1·49 + £1·49 + £1·49	£ 4·47
10	68 ÷ 7 = ▢ rem. ▢	9 rem. 5
11	0.6 + 1.8 + 0.5	2.9
12	0.1 m = ▢ cm	10 cm

B

		ANSWER
1	Write $\frac{6}{10}$ + $\frac{8}{100}$ as a decimal fraction.	0.68
2	Multiply 6 by 47.	282
3	How many cm are there in 1.8 m?	180 cm
4	Change these 24-hour clock times to 12-hour clock times. Use a.m. or p.m. (a) 06.00 (b)19.00	(a) 6.00 a.m. (b) 7.00 p.m.
5	Write 6 kg 650 g to the nearest $\frac{1}{2}$ kg.	$6\frac{1}{2}$ kg
6	Subtract 0.03 from a whole one. Write the answer as a decimal fraction.	0.97
7	By how many mm is 10.0 cm greater than 7.9 cm?	21 mm
8	Find the cost of 12 sweets if 2 sweets cost 5p.	30p
9	Find the difference between 30 multiplied by 10 and 30 divided by 10.	297
10	By how many g is 5 times 250 g less than 2 kg?	750 g
11	x y 340.4 How many times larger is the 4 marked x than the 4 marked y ?	100
12	How much greater is $\frac{7}{8}$ than $\frac{3}{4}$?	$\frac{1}{8}$

C

		ANSWER
1	Write as a decimal fraction the part of the whole square which is (a) shaded (b) unshaded.	(a) 0.21 (b) 0.79
2	How much less than £6 is the sum of £1·85 and £3·45?	70p
3	If $4\frac{1}{2}$ m of string is divided into 25-cm lengths, how many lengths will there be?	18
4	How many hundredths are equal in value to (a) 0.4 (b) 0.9?	(a) 40 hundredths (b) 90 hundredths
5	A motor cyclist travelled for $1\frac{1}{4}$ hours at a speed of 60 km/h. What distance did he travel?	75 km
6	A B Clock A shows the time. Daniel left home and clock B shows the time he returned. a.m. p.m. How many h and min was he away?	5 h 5 min
7	How many packets each with a mass of 100 g will together have a mass of $3\frac{1}{2}$ kg?	35
8	By how many twelfths is $\frac{3}{4}$ greater than $\frac{2}{3}$?	$\frac{1}{12}$
9	Find the change from a £10 note after buying 6 toys costing £1·25 each.	£ 2·50
10	Yasmin's father pays $\frac{4}{5}$ of the cost of a bicycle. Yasmin pays the remainder. The cost of the bicycle is £70. How much does each pay?	Yasmin £ 14 Father £ 56
11	200 g of meat costs 80p. Find the cost of $1\frac{1}{2}$ kg.	£ 6·00
12	The circumference of this circle is approximately 11 cm and the diameter is 3.5 cm. How much longer is the perimeter of the square than the circumference of the circle?	3 cm

Section 2   Test 8

A

		ANSWER
1	$10.0 + 0.2 + 0.05$	10.25
2	£1·60 ÷ 4	£ 0.40
3	0.47 = ▮ hundredths	47 hundredths
4	$(0 \times 9) + 8$	8
5	$(42 - 5) + (21 - 4)$	54
6	$250 + 350 + 400$	1000
7	$\frac{1}{20}$ = ▮ hundredths	$\frac{5}{100}$
8	Find $\frac{2}{3}$ of 27.	18
9	$2\frac{1}{4}$ min = ▮ s	135 s
10	£6·09 + ▮ = £8·00	£ 1·91
11	$(81 ÷ 9) - (24 ÷ 3)$	1
12	10 000 − 100	9900

B

		ANSWER	
1	Write the total of 20, $\frac{3}{10}$ and $\frac{9}{100}$ as a decimal.		20.39
2	Write in 24-hour clock times		
	(a) 3.57 a.m.	(a)	03.57
	(b) 2.20 p.m.	(b)	14.20
3	Write as a decimal the number which is 100 times smaller than 6.		0.06
4	Multiply the sum of 7 and 5 by 10.		120
5	From £2 take the total of 58p, 42p and 36p.		64p
6	Decrease 10 cm by 28 mm. Give the answer in cm.		7.2 cm
7	Write 3 ℓ 800 mℓ to the nearest $\frac{1}{2}$ ℓ.		4 ℓ
8	How many cm in		
	(a) 3.6 m	(a)	360 cm
	(b) 2.25 m?	(b)	225 cm
9	Find the cost of 750 mℓ if $\frac{1}{2}$ ℓ costs £0·74.		£ 1·11
10	Divide the product of 14 and 9 by 6.		21
11	▮4 0 9 1▮ Arrange these figures to make the largest possible odd number.		9401
12	How many hundredths are there in		
	(a) $\frac{1}{2}$	(a)	$\frac{50}{100}$
	(b) $\frac{1}{4}$	(b)	$\frac{25}{100}$
	(c) $\frac{3}{4}$?	(c)	$\frac{75}{100}$

C

		ANSWER	
1	What decimal fraction of £1 is		
	(a) 10p	(a) £	0·1
	(b) 1 p?	(b) £	0·01
2	The sum of the three angles of a triangle is 180°. Find the size in degrees of the angle marked x.		80°
3	Mother bought a doll for £1·50 and a racing car for £1·99. How much change did she receive from a £5 note?		£ 1·51
4	(a) Find in m the perimeter of the field.	(a)	500 m
	(b) How many times round the field is equal to 3 km?	(b)	6
5	Mr Jones arrived at the station at 3.45 p.m. His train left at 16.20. How long had he to wait?		35 min
6	The dial shows the mass of a parcel in kg and g. How many g less than $3\frac{1}{2}$ kg is the mass of the parcel?		800 g
7	After spending one quarter of his money Ali had 54p left. How much had he at first?		72p
8	Find the total cost of 2 packets of crisps costing 35p each and 6 biscuits costing 10p each.		£ 1·30
9	There are 163 boys in a school and there are 37 more girls than boys. How many children are there in the school altogether?		363
10	Put a decimal point in each of the numbers so that the value of the 8 is 8 units.		
	(a) 4386	(a)	438.6
	(b) 2891	(b)	28.91
11	Katie has 17p and Emily has 25p. How much must Emily give Katie so that they each have the same amount?		4p
12	$\frac{3}{8}$ of a class of 24 children are girls.		
	(a) What fraction of the class are boys?	(a)	$\frac{5}{8}$
	(b) How many boys are there?	(b)	15

Turn back to page 16 and work for the third time Progress Test 1.

Enter the result and the date on the chart.

Section 2   Test 9

A

		ANSWER
1	Write as a decimal fraction	
	(a) 17 hundredths	(a) 0.17
	(b) 6 hundredths.	(b) 0.06
2	$(58 + 5) - (4 + 9)$	50
3	$1\frac{3}{4}$ min = ▨ s	105 s
4	$80 + 6 + 8000 + ▨ = 8286$	200
5	$7 \overline{)53}$	7 rem. 4
6	0.4×100	40
7	Find $\frac{9}{10}$ of 80.	72
8	3050 g = ▨ kg ▨ g	3 kg 50 g
9	£1·00 − 28 TWOS = ▨ p	44 p
10	$7^2 - 6^2$	13
11	$(7 \times 6) + (6 \times 3)$	60
12	28p × 7	£ 1·96

B

		ANSWER
1	Write 4 ℓ 150 mℓ to the nearest $\frac{1}{2}$ litre.	4 ℓ
2	The product of two numbers is 56. One of the numbers is 7. What is the other number?	8
3	Increase 23 by 18 and multiply the answer by 10.	410
4	Find the difference between 14 plus 9 and 14 minus 9.	18
5	How much less than £1 is the sum of 18p and 39p?	43p
6	Divide the total of 19 and 17 by 4.	9
7	Write as a decimal fraction of a metre	
	(a) 20 cm	(a) 0.2 m
	(b) 35 cm.	(b) 0.35 m
8	1.20 0.12 1.02 0.21	
	Add the largest of these decimals to the smallest.	1.32
9	Write as a decimal the number which is 10 times smaller than 8.8.	0.88
10	Write each of these fractions in its lowest terms. (a) $\frac{9}{12}$ (b) $\frac{6}{8}$	(a) $\frac{3}{4}$ (b) $\frac{3}{4}$
11	Find the cost of $3\frac{1}{4}$ kg if 1 kg costs 16p.	52p
12	Write as decimals the next two numbers in this series. 1000, 100, 10, 1, ▨, ▨	0.1, 0.01

C

		ANSWER
1	What decimal fraction of £1 is	
	(a) 1 TWO	(a) £ 0·02
	(b) 1 TWENTY	(b) £ 0·2
	(c) 1 FIFTY?	(c) £ 0·5
2	Chloe is 1.35 m tall and James is 8 cm smaller. What is James's height in cm?	127 cm
3	How many bottles each holding $\frac{1}{4}$ ℓ can be filled from a cask holding $6\frac{1}{2}$ ℓ?	26
4	All the angles at the centre of the circle are equal. How many degrees are there in the marked angle?	45°
5	How many cm less than $\frac{3}{4}$ m is 0.62 m?	13 cm
6	A supermarket sold one hundred 12p plums and twenty 9p plums. What was the total value of the plums?	£ 13·80
7	Mother uses 50 g of cocoa each day. How many days will it take her to use $\frac{3}{4}$ kg?	15
8	How many g heavier is box Y than box X?	650 g
9		By how many months is
		Date of birth		(a) Ben older than Leah	(a) 11
		Sanjay 28/2/99	Ben 30/9/97	Leah 30/8/98	(b) Sanjay younger than Leah	(b) 6
10	Two angles of a triangle each measure 45°. Find the size in degrees of the third angle.	90°
11	Amy's T-shirt cost £12·70 and George's cost £11·85. Find	
	(a) the difference in price	(a) 85p
	(b) the total cost of the T-shirts.	(b) £ 24·55
12	1 cm on a plan represents 1 m. What does 1 mm on the plan represent	
	(a) in cm	(a) 10 cm
	(b) in mm?	(b) 100 mm

Section 2 Test 10

A

		ANSWER
1	500 g × 10 = ▢ kg	5 kg
2	(36 − 7) − (32 − 8)	5
3	1000p = £ ▢	£ 10
4	£ ▢ + 62p = £3·00	£ 2·38
5	9) $\overline{x}$ 6 rem. 2 Find x.	56
6	Write 243 hundredths as a decimal.	2.43
7	(10 × 5) − (4 × 7)	22
8	$\frac{1}{10}$ of 1 min = ▢ s	6 s
9	$\frac{5}{8}$ of 64 km	40 km
10	10 articles cost 19p. 100 articles cost £ ▢.	£ 1·90
11	612 ÷ y = 6. Find y.	102
12	9989 + 12	10 001

B

		ANSWER
1	Write 41p as (a) a vulgar fraction of £1	(a) £ $\frac{41}{100}$
	(b) a decimal fraction of £1.	(b) £ 0·41
2	Make each of these numbers 10 times smaller. (a) 29	(a) 2.9
	(b) 1.7	(b) 0.17
3	Write in 24-hour clock time quarter to five in the afternoon.	16.45
4	How much more than a FIFTY is the sum of 8p, 18p and 28p?	4 p
5	Subtract 9 from the total of 53 and 47.	91
6	$\frac{3}{8}$ of a number is 9. What is the number?	24
7	Write these fractions in their lowest terms. (a) $\frac{25}{100}$ (b) $\frac{15}{20}$	(a) $\frac{1}{4}$ (b) $\frac{3}{4}$
8	What is the change from £5 after spending £1·36 and £2·40?	£ 1·24
9	If 10 models cost £5·20, what will be the cost of (a) 1	(a) 52 p
	(b) 7?	(b) £ 3·64
10	$\frac{1}{5} = \frac{x}{100}$ $\frac{3}{5} = \frac{y}{100}$ Find the value of x and y.	x 20
		y 60
11	1 ℓ costs 60p. Find the cost of $5\frac{1}{4}$ ℓ.	£ 3·15
12	If wool costs 80p for 50 g, what is the cost of $\frac{1}{2}$ kg?	£ 8·00

C

		ANSWER
1	Find the total of 3.8 m and 0.5 m (a) in cm	(a) 430 cm
	(b) in mm.	(b) 4300 mm
2	The four angles of any quadrilateral together equal 360°. Find in degrees the size of the angles marked x.	130°
3	Nadeen saved a FIFTY each week for a whole year. How much did she save altogether?	£ 26
4	M1 LONDON 75 km — If a tanker travels at a steady speed of 50 km/h how long will it take to reach London?	$1\frac{1}{2}$ h
5	5.5 0.2 0.55 0.02 Which of these decimals is equal to (a) $\frac{55}{100}$ (b) $\frac{2}{100}$?	(a) 0.55 (b) 0.02
6	Name the three coins given in change from £4 after spending £3·77.	20p 2p 1p
7	What remains from a 10-metre length of cloth after using 3.3 m and 2.8 m?	3.9 m
8	Each side of this shape is 0.7 cm long. Find the perimeter of the shape in cm.	7 cm
9	After spending 49p and £1·36 Amy has 15p left. How much had she at first?	£ 2·00
10	What time will be shown on the clock after 47 min? Use a.m. or p.m.	12.22 p.m.
11	Find the difference between $\frac{1}{10}$ of 7000 and $\frac{1}{100}$ of 7000.	630
12	A school outing will cost Ryan £10·80. He has made 8 weekly payments of £1·20. How much has he yet to pay?	£ 1·20

27

A

		ANSWER
1	£2·26 + £1·87	£ 4·13
2	5.4 m = ☐ m + 140 cm	4 m
3	(35 ÷ 7) × (30 ÷ 6)	25
4	$3\,\ell\,300\,m\ell - \frac{1}{2}\ell$ = ☐ ℓ ☐ $m\ell$	2 ℓ 800 $m\ell$
5	135 min = ☐ h ☐ min	2 h 15 min
6	45p + 29p + ☐ p = £1	26p
7	(8 + 56) − (15 + 9)	40
8	0.75 m × 100	75 m
9	(40 ÷ 8) × 7	35
10	2 kg 750 g + 900 g = ☐ kg ☐ g	3 kg 650 g
11	(a) $\frac{1}{4}$ km = ☐ m	(a) 250 m
	(b) $\frac{3}{4}$ km = ☐ m	(b) 750 m
12	Find $\frac{5}{6}$ of 30 ℓ.	25 ℓ

B

		ANSWER
1	Find the product of 7 and 18.	126
2	Find the number which is 100 times smaller than (a) 240	(a) 2.4
	(b) 37.	(b) 0.37
3	Write as cm (a) 3.25 m	(a) 325 cm
	(b) 4.06 m.	(b) 406 cm
4	How many grams more than $\frac{1}{2}$ kg is the sum of 280 g and 270 g?	50 g
5	What must be added to 39 to make 57?	18
6	Decrease 43 by 16 and multiply the answer by 10.	270
7	From the sum of £1·17 and £1·33 subtract 60p.	£ 1·90
8	Find the remainder when 113 is divided by 6.	5
9	Write as a decimal fraction of a kg (a) 500 g	(a) 0.5 kg
	(b) 100 g.	(b) 0.1 kg
10	1 pencil costs 9p. Find the cost of 200 pencils.	£ 18·00
11	What is the perimeter of a rectangle 7 metres long and $6\frac{1}{2}$ metres wide?	27 m
12	How many newspapers each costing 40p can be bought for £8·00?	20

C

		ANSWER
1	Find in degrees the measurement of each of the angles a and b.	a 60°
		b 140°
2	How many TWOS have the same value as (a) 12 FIVES	(a) 30
	(b) 3 FIFTIES?	(b) 75
3	Write all the numbers between 48 and 68 which can be divided by 7 without a remainder.	49 56 63
4	10 boxes have a mass of $1\frac{1}{2}$ kg. Find the mass in g of (a) 1 box	(a) 150 g
	(b) 5 boxes.	(b) 750 g
5	Brotley ←— 45 km —→ Carley A cyclist started from Brotley at 11.30 a.m. and arrived at Carley at 2.30 p.m. If he travelled at the same rate, what was his speed in km/h?	15 km/h
6	Katie's mother gave her £1·45 to add to her savings and her father gave her £2·70. She then had £5. How much had she at first?	85p
7	BRONCO RADIOS LIST PRICE £18 Radios are reduced by 10p in the £ off the list price. What is the new price?	£ 16·20
8	There are 186 pages in a book. Tom read 64 pages and then 56 pages. How many more pages has he to read?	66
9	10.0 1.04 1.96 1.11 0.99 Multiply the largest of these numbers by the smallest.	9.9
10	In a class of 32 children $\frac{3}{8}$ of them are 10 years old, $\frac{1}{2}$ are 9 and the rest are 8 years old. (a) What fraction of the children are 8?	(a) $\frac{1}{8}$
	(b) How many children are 8?	(b) 4
11	The circumference of a wheel is 1.85 m. Find in m the distance the wheel will travel in (a) 10 turns	(a) 18.5 m
	(b) 100 turns.	(b) 185 m
12	3 kg of meat cost £18·00. Find the cost of (a) 500 g	(a) £ 3
	(b) 750 g.	(b) £ 4·50

Turn back to page 16 and work for the fourth time Progress Test 1.

Enter the result and the date on the chart.

Section 2 Test 12

A

		ANSWER
1	290 cm = ▢ m	2.9 m
2	(82 − 4) + (18 − 9)	87
3	(17 × 3) + 6	57
4	$\frac{28}{4}$ = ▢ whole ones	7
5	1 article costs £0·07. 100 articles cost £ ▢ .	£ 7·00
6	346 + 78	424
7	$\frac{1}{10}$ of 9 km = ▢ m	900 m
8	5)£10·10	£ 2·02
9	£2·00 − 25 FIVES	75p
10	$10^2 - 9^2$	19
11	Write £8·84 (a) to the nearest 10p	(a) £ 8·80
	(b) to the nearest £.	(b) £ 9·00
12	£10·00 ÷ 8	£ 1·25

B

		ANSWER
1	Write as ℓ and mℓ (a) 3457 mℓ	(a) 3 ℓ 457 mℓ
	(b) 4070 mℓ.	(b) 4 ℓ 70 mℓ
2	Find the difference between (15 + 15 + 15) and (4 × 15).	15
3	52 plus 70 minus 32	90
4	Divide the total of 29 and 27 by 8.	7
5	Subtract 6 times 14p from £1.	16p
6	How much greater is 7 multiplied by 9 than 7 plus 9?	47
7	Find in cm the perimeter of a triangle having equal sides each measuring 48 mm.	14.4 cm
8	How many h and min from 11.40 to 18.10?	6 h 30 min
9	Write as a decimal fraction (a) $\frac{1}{4}$	(a) 0.25
	(b) $\frac{3}{4}$.	(b) 0.75
10	0.3 0.15 0.09 1.1 0.99 Add the smallest of these decimals to the largest.	1.19
11	If 10 cost £2·70, what is the cost of 1?	27p
12	Find the cost of 300 g if $\frac{1}{2}$ kg costs 30p.	18p

C

		ANSWER
1	How many small squares are there in $\frac{7}{10}$ of this diagram?	70
2	765 884 670 Which of these numbers will divide by 2, 5 and 10 without a remainder?	670
3	By putting in a decimal point make (a) the 5 in 2056 equal to 5 tenths	(a) 20.56
	(b) the 7 in 1870 equal to 7 hundredths.	(b) 1.870
4	A 1p coin has a mass of 3.56 grams. Find the mass of (a) 100 coins	(a) 356 g
	(b) 50 coins.	(b) 178 g
5	$\frac{5}{8}$ of a sum of money is £1·10. What is the whole amount?	£ 1·76
6	How many bottles each holding 150 mℓ can be filled from a can holding $1\frac{1}{2}$ ℓ ?	10
7	This is a sketch map of a park. What is the perimeter of the park in km? (500 m, 400 m, 800 m, 700 m)	2.4 km
8	£3·73 £3·54 £3·37 £3·36 £3·63 Which two of these amounts when added together equal £7?	£ 3·37 £ 3·63
9	Sophie and Olivia shared 60p so that Olivia had 10p more than Sophie. How much did Sophie have?	25p
10	Write as a decimal fraction the part of the circle which is (a) shaded	(a) 0.6
	(b) unshaded.	(b) 0.4
11	The length of a steel rod is 1.75 m. Write the length of a rod 4 times as long.	7 m
12	PET FOOD LARGE TINS (340 g) 67p EACH SMALL TINS (170 g) 10 for £3·50 How much is saved when buying 10 large tins rather than 20 small tins?	30p

Next work Progress Test 2 on page 30.

Enter the result and the date on the chart.

PROGRESS TEST 2

Write the numbers 1 to 20 down the side of a sheet of paper.
Write alongside these numbers the **answers only** to the following questions.
Work as quickly as you can.
Time allowed – **10 minutes.**

1   Write the sum of £0·44, £0·56 and £1·55 to the nearest TEN.   £2·60

2   The circle is divided into three equal parts. How many degrees are there in the angle marked at the centre?   120°

3   A car travelled for 15 minutes at a speed of 48 km/h. What distance did it travel?   12 km

4   The circumference of a wheel is 1.25 m. How many m will it travel in 10 turns?   12.5 m

5   Make 306 one hundred times smaller.   3.06

6   Write as a decimal the total of 20, $\frac{8}{10}$ and $\frac{19}{100}$.   20.99

7   Subtract $\frac{2}{9}$ of 27 from $\frac{3}{5}$ of 45.   21

8   Clock A is 10 minutes fast. How many minutes slow is clock B?   20 min

9   By how many m is 648 m less than $\frac{3}{4}$ km?   102 m

10   Write the decimal fraction which is half-way between 0.4 and 0.38.   0.39

11 | 8 9 9 9 . 4 | This reading is taken from a dial in a car. It shows the number of km travelled. What will be the reading after travelling a further 700 m?   9000.1 km

12   If one article costs £0·44 what will be the cost of 100?   £44·00

13   Find the cost of $4\frac{3}{4}$ kg at 40p per kg.   £1·90

14   By how many sixths is $\frac{1}{2}$ less than $\frac{2}{3}$? $\frac{1}{6}$

15   Which 3 coins were given in change from £3 after spending £1·28 and £1·56?   10p 5p 1p

16 $3\frac{1}{2}$ litres + 900 mℓ + 600 mℓ = ⬜ ℓ   5 ℓ

17

   Which of these 24-hour clock times is nearest to twenty to seven in the evening?   Y

18   How many g more than $\frac{1}{2}$ kg is the sum of 334 g and 286 g?   120 g

19   50 cm of tape cost 28p. Find the cost of 1.25 m.   70p

20 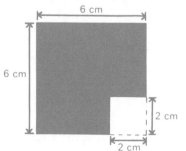   Find in cm the perimeter of the shaded shape.   24 cm

PROGRESS TEST 2

RESULTS CHART

You will work Progress Test 2 at **four** different times. When you first work the test
    (a) colour the first column to show the number of examples correct out of 20
    (b) enter the date.
Each time you work the test, enter the result and the date in the marked columns.

number of examples correct	1st	2nd	3rd	4th
20				
19				
18				
17				
16				
15				
14				
13				
12				
11				
10				
9				
8				
7				
6				
5				
4				
3				
2				
1				
0				
date				

Section 3 Test 1

A

		ANSWER
1	Th H T U How many less than six thousand is the number shown on the abacus picture?	90
2	4 km 720 m = ☐ m	4720 m
3	35p × 10 = £ ☐	£ 3·50
4	$\frac{1}{2}\ell$ − 340 mℓ = ☐ mℓ	160 mℓ
5	50p + 50p + 50p + 35p = £ ☐	£ 1·85
6	23 + 9 + 18	50
7	2 h 25 min = ☐ min	145 min
8	£5·70 = ☐ TENS	57 TENS
9	$1\frac{1}{2}$ kg − ☐ g = 650 g	850 g
10	$\frac{3}{4} + \frac{3}{4} + \frac{1}{2}$	2
11	32.4 cm = ☐ mm	324 mm
12	$\frac{3}{4}$ of 8 ℓ	6 ℓ

B

		ANSWER
1	Write in figures: four thousand two hundred and four.	4204
2	Subtract £0·49 from £1·00.	51p
3	Find the average of 6, 8 and 10.	8
4	What is the cost of 8 pencils at 2 for 17p?	68p
5	50 cm is cut off a 3.5-m roll of ribbon. How many metres are left?	3 m
6	Divide £1·28 by 8.	16p
7	Change to 24-hour clock times (a) 11.55 a.m.	(a) 11.55
	(b) 1.40 p.m.	(b) 13.40
8	Subtract $\frac{1}{3}$ of 30p from $\frac{1}{2}$ of 30p.	5p
9	How many mℓ in 0.5 ℓ?	500 mℓ
10	┌─────────────────────┐ │ 12 24 33 18 │ └─────────────────────┘ Which of these numbers can be divided by 2, 3, 6 and 9 without a remainder?	18
11	What fraction, in its lowest terms, is 400 m of 1 km?	$\frac{2}{5}$
12	Find the difference between 0.3 and 0.03	0.27

C

		ANSWER
1	How much change from £1·00 after buying 8 labels at 9p each?	28p
2	Angle ABC is a right angle. How many degrees are there in the angle marked y?	44°
3	Tom had 40 marbles. He lost 16 and then won 24. How many marbles had he then?	48
4	What fraction of this strip is (a) shaded (b) unshaded?	(a) $\frac{5}{7}$ (b) $\frac{2}{7}$
5	Write these times in figures using a.m. or p.m. (a) $2\frac{1}{4}$ hours after 10.00 a.m. (b) 7 hours after 7.00 pm	(a) 12.15 p.m. (b) 2.00 a.m.
6	Find, to the nearest km, the total distance from Bant to Crock. 18.7 km 19.9 km Bistow Bant Crock	39 km
7	James saved £1·25 each week for 8 weeks. How much did he save?	£ 10·00
8	How many g less than 4 kg is the total mass of 10 parcels each having a mass of 345 g?	550 g
9	marbles Large 6p each Small 4p each Find the total cost of 6 large marbles and 6 small marbles.	60p
10	A car travelled at an average speed of 90 km/h for $1\frac{1}{2}$ hours. What distance did it travel?	135 km
11	By counting the squares find which of the shapes has (a) the largest area (b) the smallest area.	(a) Z (b) Y
12	V W **8 0 8 0** How many times larger is the 8 marked V than the 8 marked W?	100

Section 3   Test 2

A

		ANSWER
1	8 + 7000 + = 7808	800
2	£6·00 − £1·95 = £	£ 4·05
3	46 × 6	276
4	$7\overline{)749}^{\,x}$ Find the value of x.	107
5	85p + p = £1·15	30p
6	5 kg 60 g = g	5060 g
7	7 cm − 1.5 cm = mm	55 mm
8	£9·00 ÷ 100 = p	9p
9	2.75 m = m cm	2 m 75 cm
10	$\frac{4}{5}$ of 35 kg	28 kg
11	200 min = h min	3 h 20 min
12	$\frac{1}{4}$ kg + 130 g + g = $\frac{1}{2}$ kg	120 g

B

		ANSWER
1	Divide the sum of 53 and 65 by 2.	59
2	The change from £2·00 was 43p. How much had been spent?	£ 1·57
3	Find the product of 8 and 8.	64
4	10 gift cards cost £1·20. Find the cost of 1 card.	12p
5	Write the next two numbers of this series. 0.2 0.4 0.6 0.8	1.0, 1.2
6	From 360° subtract the sum of two right angles.	180°
7	How many km and m are equal to 1560 m?	1 km 560 m
8	Write $9\frac{3}{8}$ to the nearest whole number.	9
9	Change to 12-hour clock times. Use a.m. or p.m. (a) 15.45	(a) 3.45 p.m.
	(b) 00.15	(b) 12.15 a.m.
10	How many whole ones are equal to 36 quarters?	9
11	How many tens have the same value as 5010?	501
12	The sum of two numbers is 17. The difference between them is 1. What are the two numbers?	8 9

C

		ANSWER
1	Find the change from £5 after spending £1·33 and £2·57.	£ 1·10
2	A car travelled 240 km in 3 hours. What was the average speed in km/h?	80 km/h
3	14 kg 10 kg 9 kg — Find the average mass of the three boxes.	11 kg
4	Grapes cost £3·60 per kg. What is the cost of 2 kg 500 g?	£ 9·00
5	By counting the small squares find the two shapes which are equal in area. Name the two shapes.	rectangle triangle
6	Josh had 150 stamps. He put 15 stamps on each of 8 pages in his album. How many stamps had he left?	30
7	This clock is 15 minutes fast. Write the correct time in figures using a.m. or p.m. morning	9.53 a.m.
8	A pack of 4 tins of ham can be bought for £5·12. Find the cost of 1 tin.	£ 1·28
9	At a football match there were 12 498 spectators. Write the number of spectators (a) to the nearest hundred	(a) 12 500
	(b) to the nearest thousand.	(b) 12 000
10	 These angles are equal. (a) How many right angles are equal to the sum of the five angles?	(a) 4
	(b) How many degrees are there in each of the five angles?	(b) 72°
11	Share 80p between Ali and Katie so that Ali has 20p more than Katie.	Ali 50p Katie 30p
12	There were 2.5 ℓ of milk for 4 children. 100 mℓ were spilt and the remainder was divided equally. What was one share?	600 mℓ

Section 3　Test 3

A

		ANSWER
1	9999 + 9	10 008
2	25 + 26 = 11 +	40
3	368 cm = ▢ m	3.68 m
4	£1·17 × 7	£ 8·19
5	▢ p × 10 = £1·40	14p
6	$\frac{1}{2} + \frac{1}{8}$	$\frac{5}{8}$
7	6)£4·02	£ 0·67
8	5.7 ℓ = ▢ mℓ	5700 mℓ
9	4 weeks = ▢ days	28
10	3.21 × 100	321
11	▢ × 7 = 37 − 9	4
12	1.7 cm + 4.5 cm = ▢ mm	62 mm

B

		ANSWER
1	£1·84 × 10. Write the answer to the nearest £.	£ 18
2	Take two hundred from 22 222.	22 022
3	Write 600 m as a decimal fraction of 1 km.	0.6 km
4	How many times larger is £2·50 than 25p?	10
5	Divide 912 by 4.	228
6	Write as a decimal fraction the difference between 0.1 and a half.	0.4
7	How many days altogether in April and May?	61
8	Write the next two numbers in this series. 8.0, 8.5, 9.0, 9.5, ▢,	10.0, 10.5
9	By how many cm is $\frac{1}{10}$ m longer than $\frac{1}{100}$ m?	9 cm
10	200 mℓ cost 15p. Find the cost of 1 ℓ.	75p
11	Find the difference in g between 1.7 kg and 2.5 kg.	800 g
12	Write the missing signs +, −, × or ÷ in place of ● and ▲. 6 ● 3 = 9 ▲ 9	● × ▲ +

C

		ANSWER
1	Th H T U How many must be added to the number shown on the abacus picture to make four thousand?	450
2	How long will it take a truck travelling at an average speed of 60 km/h to travel a distance of 360 km?	6 h
3	How many right angles are equal to the sum of the three angles of a triangle?	2
4	Katie wrote an answer of £0.60 instead of £0·06. By how many pence was her answer wrong?	54p
5	6 cm 3 cm Find (a) the area (b) the perimeter of the rectangle. In each case give the unit of measurement. (a)	18 cm²
		(b) 18 cm
6	In a school dining room there were 25 tables each set with 6 places. 11 of the places were not used. How many stayed for dinner?	139
7	HOME SCHOOL The diagram shows the time a boy spends at home and at school. What fraction of his time does he spend (a) at home (b) at school?	(a) $\frac{7}{12}$ (b) $\frac{5}{12}$
8	In James' money box there were 30 TWENTIES and twice as many TENS. How much was that altogether?	£ 12
9	Write the mass shown by the pointer (a) in kg and g (b) in kg as a decimal.	(a) 2 kg 800 g (b) 2.8 kg
10	In a school of 57 children, there is a small class of 9 children and two classes of equal numbers. How many children are there in each of the larger classes?	24
11	How many mℓ more does a can containing 2.5 ℓ hold than the total contents of two cans each holding 850 mℓ?	800 mℓ
12	SWEETS 12p each or 10 for £1·10 How much is saved on each sweet by buying 10 at a time?	1p

34

Section 3 Test 4

A

		ANSWER
1	270 mℓ + 300 mℓ	570 mℓ
2	10 000 − 100	9 900
3	4.93 m = ☐ cm	493 cm
4	$\frac{7}{10}$ of £1 = ☐ p	70p
5	3.93 + 0.07	4
6	6.06 = $\frac{☐}{100}$	$\frac{606}{100}$
7	0.7 kg + 0.4 kg = ☐ kg ☐ g	1 kg 100 g
8	$\frac{☐}{2}$ = $9\frac{1}{2}$	$\frac{19}{2}$
9	$\frac{1}{3} - \frac{1}{6}$	$\frac{1}{6}$
10	£1·30 ÷ ☐ = 10p	13
11	From 11.25 a.m. to 12.45 p.m. = ☐ min.	80 min
12	1 kg 700 g × 5 = ☐ kg	8.5 kg

B

		ANSWER
1	Write as a decimal (a) $3\frac{1}{10}$ (b) $4\frac{8}{10}$.	(a) 3.1 (b) 4.8
2	How many FIVES must be added to 5 FIFTIES to make £2·80?	6
3	Write 268 mm to the nearest cm.	27 cm
4	Which two of these fractions are of equal value? $\frac{2}{3}$ $\frac{1}{4}$ $\frac{4}{8}$ $\frac{4}{6}$ $\frac{3}{4}$	$\frac{2}{3}$ $\frac{4}{6}$
5	$1\frac{1}{4}$ ℓ of a 2-ℓ can are used. How many mℓ are left?	750 mℓ
6	The average of 3 numbers is 9. What is the total of the three numbers?	27
7	How many years from 1985 to the year 2000?	15
8	Josh has completed 4.4 km of a 5-km journey. How many metres has he still to travel?	600 m
9	Multiply 1.8 by 5.	9
10	How many times shorter is 15 cm than 1.5 m?	10
11	2 biscuits cost 15p. Find the cost of half a dozen.	45p
12	A square has sides each 9 cm long. What is the area of the square? Give the unit of measurement.	81 cm²

C

		ANSWER
1	After losing 25 marbles, Lucy had 9 blue and 8 red ones left. How many had she at first?	42
2	$\frac{5}{9}$ of this rectangle is shaded. What fraction is unshaded?	$\frac{4}{9}$
3	To pay for two pens costing 75p and 85p Mandeep gave the shopkeeper two £1 coins and a TEN. What coin did he receive in change?	50p
4	The ruler is marked in mm. Write, in cm, the length of each line Y and Z.	Y 5.6 cm Z 4.8 cm
5	James had £4·00 spending money. He spent 80p each day. For how many days did his money last?	5
6	How many grams must be added to the scale pan to make 4 kg?	700 g
7	Josh's holiday is from the 18th January until the 13th February inclusive of both dates. How many days is that?	27
8	Find the average number of dots in a row.	5
9	Mrs Jones travelled on a motorway from 11.00 a.m. to 12.15 p.m. Her average speed was 100 km/h. What distance did she travel?	125 km
10	How many degrees are there in the angle marked y?	60
11	How much change from £5 after buying 8 tins of fruit at 55p each?	60p
12	How far is it round a rectangular playground which is 75 m long and 60 m wide?	270 m

Turn back to page 30 and work for the second time Progress Test 2.

Enter the result and the date on the chart.

35

Section 3 Test 5

A

		ANSWER
1	2.9 = ☐ tenths	29 tenths
2	£4·07 = ☐ p	407p
3	3 h 50 min = ☐ min	230 min
4	24p × 5 = £☐	£ 1·20
5	7 × ☐ = 43 − 8	5
6	76p + 5 FIVES = £☐	£ 1·01
7	(1000 × 10) + (100 × 5) + (10 × 7)	10 570
8	5.08 m = ☐ cm	508 cm
9	Find $\frac{1}{2}$ of $3\frac{1}{2}$.	$1\frac{3}{4}$
10	0.6 kg − ☐ g = 340 g	260 g
11	$3\frac{3}{4}\ell$ = ☐ ℓ ☐ mℓ	3 ℓ 750 mℓ
12	11p × 100 = £☐	£ 11·00

B

		ANSWER
1	Find the missing number in this series. 1, 10, 100, ☐, 10 000	1000
2	Find the product of 10 and 45.	450
3	How many times greater than 0.1 is 10?	100
4	What distance in km and m is twice as long as 4.8 km?	9 km 600 m
5	Divide 52p exactly by 4.	13p
6	Find the difference in pence between 15 TENS and 40 FIVES.	50p
7	A journey of 7 km cost 91p. How much was the charge per km?	13p
8	Write to the nearest $\frac{1}{2}$ kg (a) 1 kg 620 g	(a) $1\frac{1}{2}$ kg
	(b) 2 kg 390 g.	(b) $2\frac{1}{2}$ kg
9	Find the area of a rectangle 7 cm long and 3 cm wide. Give the unit of measurement.	21 cm²
10	By how many pence is $\frac{1}{5}$ of £3 greater than $\frac{1}{6}$ of £3?	10p
11	58 cm divided by 10 = ☐ mm.	58 mm
12	Write as a decimal fraction of a kg the sum of $\frac{1}{4}$ kg and 450 g.	0.7 kg

C

		ANSWER
1	What decimal fraction must be added to the number shown on the abacus picture to equal 50?	0.5
2	What fraction of 28 kg is (a) 7 kg (b) 4 kg?	(a) $\frac{1}{4}$ (b) $\frac{1}{7}$
3	☐18/6/93☐ By how many months is 18 February 1994 later than the given date?	8 months
4	Write a quarter of a metre (a) in cm	(a) 25 cm
	(b) as a decimal fraction of a metre.	(b) 0.25 m
5	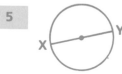 The radius of this circle is 0.9 cm. Find the length of the line XY in mm.	18 mm
6	☐ $\frac{5}{6}$ $\frac{5}{7}$ $\frac{5}{8}$ $\frac{5}{9}$ $\frac{5}{10}$ ☐ Which of these fractions is (a) the largest (b) the smallest?	(a) $\frac{5}{6}$ (b) $\frac{5}{10}$
7	A cyclist travelled 72 km in 3 hours. What was his average speed in km/h?	24 km/h
8	 The perimeter of this regular hexagon is 7.2 cm. Find the length of one side (a) in cm	(a) 1.2 cm
	(b) in mm.	(b) 12 mm

9 |

PRICE CHART	mass	100g	150g	200g	250g	300g
	cost	18p	x	36p	y	54p

Find the value in pence of x and y.

x 27p y 45p

10	How many degrees are there in the angle marked x ?	70°
11	Amounts spent: Tom 10p Katie 20p Salma 40p Daniel 30p. Find the average amount spent by the children.	25p
12	Daniel takes four 5-mℓ spoonfuls of medicine each day. For how many days will 0.2 ℓ last him?	10 days

Section 3   Test 6

A		ANSWER
1	☐ + 6 + 9000 + 400 = 9456	50
2	$\frac{4}{5}$ = ☐ hundredths	$\frac{80}{100}$
3	£4·05 − 50p = £ ☐	£ 3·55
4	24 + 24 + 24 + 24 + 24 + 24 + 24	168
5	1 ℓ 600 mℓ ÷ 8 = ☐ mℓ	200 mℓ
6	£3·60 ÷ 10 = ☐ p	36p
7	9.6 cm − 15 mm = ☐ mm	81 mm
8	£3·10 = 3 FIFTIES + ☐ TWENTIES	8 TWENTIES
9	$10^2 − 5^2$	75
10	8 km − 1700 m = ☐ km	6.3 km
11	$\frac{3}{4}$ kg − 260 g = ☐ g	490 g
12	$\frac{5}{7}$ of £63	£ 45

B		ANSWER
1	How many times greater is £8 than 8p?	100
2	Find the diameter of a circle the radius of which is (a) 5.5 cm (b) 46 mm.	(a) 11 cm (b) 92 mm
3	Reduce 125 by 99.	26
4	How many hundreds are there in 10 000?	100
5	Multiply 55p by 10.	£ 5·50
6	How many hours in 3 days?	72
7	Write in £s the total of 7 FIVES, 4 TENS and 9 TWOS.	£ 0·93
8	500 g cost 28p. Find the cost of $1\frac{1}{2}$ kg.	84p
9	Multiply 9.5 cm by 100. Write the answer in m.	9.5 m
10	Write the sum of $4\frac{7}{10}$ and $3\frac{9}{10}$ as a decimal.	8.6
11	$\frac{3}{4}$ of a number is 9. What is the number?	12
12	A 4-m length of ribbon is cut into 5 equal pieces. Find the length in cm of one piece.	80 cm

C		ANSWER
1	How much change from a FIFTY after buying 4 badges at 9p each?	14p
2	Write as a decimal fraction the difference between $\frac{9}{10}$ and $\frac{99}{100}$.	0.09
3	How many mℓ remain from 2 ℓ after filling the 3 bottles? (650 mℓ, 650 mℓ, 650 mℓ)	50 mℓ
4	15th of November was on a Wednesday. On which day of the week was the 29th of November?	Wednesday
5	An aircraft left Gatwick at 11.00 and by 13.00 it had travelled 1850 km. What was its average speed in km/h?	925 km/h
6	Write the number nearest to 99 which can be divided exactly by 8.	96
7	Munch Bars are 63p for a packet of 6. Find the cost of 2 bars.	21p
8	Mandeep 9, Emily 7, Sam ☐, Jessica 6. In a test the average score of the four children was 8. What was Sam's score?	10
9	The length of Hassan's pace is 50 cm. How many paces does he take when walking 1 km?	2000
10	Name this triangle (45°, 45°) (a) by its angles (b) by its sides.	(a) right-angled triangle (b) isosceles triangle
11	(850g W, 0.8kg X, 0.9kg Y, 650g Z) Which two of the boxes together have a mass of 1.5 kg?	W Z
12	$6\overline{)x}$ 19 rem. 5 Find the value of x.	119

Section 3 Test 7

A | | ANSWER

#			ANSWER
1	1.6 = (a) tenths	(a)	16 tenths
	(b) hundredths	(b)	160 hundredths
2	$\frac{11}{16}$ + = 1		$\frac{5}{16}$
3	23 + 25 = × 6		8
4	0.78 m = cm		78 cm
5	57 ÷ 3		19
6	£1·00 − (23p + 38p)		39p
7	(6 × 6) − (3 × 9)		9
8	£3·50 × 8 = £		£ 28·00
9	5.6 cm − 38 mm = mm		18 mm
10	7 FIVES = TWOS + 1p		17 TWOS
11	10 articles cost £2·50. One will cost p.		25p
12	1 kg 600 g + 3 kg 800 g = kg		5.4 kg

B | | ANSWER

#			ANSWER
1	Write 864 cm to the nearest m.		9 m
2	Increase £4·55 by 90p.		£ 5·45
3	Find the radius in cm of a circle which has a diameter of (a) 68 mm	(a)	3.4 cm
	(b) 3.6 cm.	(b)	1.8 cm
4	Reduce each fraction to its lowest terms. (a) $\frac{15}{20}$		
	(b) $\frac{12}{16}$ (a) $\frac{3}{4}$	(b)	$\frac{3}{4}$
5	Write as a decimal the total of 3 tens, 7 tenths and 8 hundredths.		30.78
6	Find the missing numbers in this series. 90, 81, , ,54, 45	72,	63
7	$\frac{54}{6}$ = 36 ÷ Y. Find the value of Y.		4
8	Find the difference between £0·50 and one quarter of £1.		25p
9	What fraction of 10 is $1\frac{1}{4}$?		$\frac{1}{8}$
10	Divide £8·40 by 10 and add 16p to the answer.		£ 1·00
11	3.6 kg × 6. Write the answer to the nearest kg.		22 kg
12	Find one quarter of 10 metres (a) in m	(a)	2.5 m
	(b) in cm.	(b)	250 cm

C | | ANSWER

#			ANSWER
1	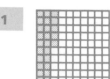 Write the part of the square which is shaded (a) as a decimal fraction	(a)	0.25
	(b) as a vulgar fraction in its lowest terms. (b)		$\frac{1}{4}$

2 Which number other than 1 will divide exactly into each of these numbers?

28	42	35	14

7

3  Find the measurement in degrees of the angle marked Y.   40°

4 A litre of water has a mass of 1 kg. Find the mass in g of. (a) 0.5 ℓ   (a) 500 g

(b) $\frac{1}{4}$ ℓ.   (b) 250 g

5 What is the area of a corridor $2\frac{1}{2}$ m wide and 20 m long? Give the unit of measurement.   50 m²

6

TIME-TABLE	
LEAVE BORDEN	ARRIVE NOTLEY
X	17.30	18.03
Y	18.30	19.03
Z	19.30	20.03

Which bus X, Y or Z
(a) arrives Notley at 7.03 p.m. (a)   Y
(b) leaves Borden at 7.30 p.m.? (b)   Z

7 25 cm of tape cost 14p. Find the cost per m.   56p

8 Katie bought 4 pencils each costing 18p. Name the three coins she gave in exact payment.   50p 20p 2p

9 How many 250-mℓ bottles can be filled from $2\frac{1}{2}$ ℓ?   10

10

MON.	TUES.	WED.	THURS.	FRI.
7	11	10	6	6

The chart shows the number of minutes Daniel took to walk to school each day. Find his average time.   8 min

11 A lorry travelled at an average speed of 60 km/h for a distance of 75 km. How long did the journey take?   1 h 15 min

12

The diagram shows the lengths of the roads from Mandeep's to Hassan's house. Find the total distance in (a) km   (a) 5.7 km

(b) m.   (b) 5700 m

Section 3 Test 8

A

		ANSWER
1	39 + 67	106
2	0.1 + 10 + 0.06	10.16
3	2 h − 28 min = min	92 min
4	500 − (40 × 9)	140
5	9 cm ÷ 10 = mm	9 mm
6	$\frac{3}{5} + \frac{3}{10}$	$\frac{9}{10}$
7	(9 × 6) + (3 × 8)	78
8	mℓ × 10 = 4 ℓ	400 mℓ
9	1.4 kg − 850 g = g	550 g
10	£1 − (8p × 6) = p	52p
11	$\frac{7}{8}$ of £56	£ 49
12	6 metres ÷ 4 = cm	150 cm

B

		ANSWER
1	Write to the nearest whole number (a) 8.5 (b) $11\frac{5}{12}$.	(a) 9 (b) 11
2	Write 39p as a decimal fraction of £1.	£ 0·39
3	How many times can 0.2 be taken from 1?	5
4	How many days in (a) a year (b) a leap year?	(a) 365 (b) 366
5	What sum of money is equal to 5 times 88p?	£ 4·40
6	Which of these fractions is equal to $\frac{3}{4}$? $\frac{16}{20}$ $\frac{15}{20}$ $\frac{16}{24}$ $\frac{12}{18}$	$\frac{15}{20}$
7	Find the difference in g between $\frac{1}{2}$ kg and 0.3 kg.	200 g
8	Multiply 8.33 m by 100.	833 m
9	By how many cm is 2.46 m greater than 1.95 m?	51 cm
10	Find the average of 8, 13, 10 and 9.	10
11	By how many is the sum of 15 and 10 less than the product of 15 and 10?	125
12	**4,0,8,7** Re-arrange these figures to make the largest possible even number.	8740

C

		ANSWER
1	How many g less than 5 kg is the total of 2.7 kg and 1.5 kg?	800 g
2	Find (a) the diameter (b) the radius of the largest circle which can be drawn in this square. 16 mm	(a) 16 mm (b) 8 mm
3	How many 7p sweets can be bought for £2·10?	30
4	The perimeter of this triangle is 75 mm. Find the length of the side AB.	34 mm
5	Which 3 coins are given in change from £5 after spending £4·76?	20p 2p 2p
6	Write the amount of liquid in this jug as (a) a decimal fraction of 1 ℓ (b) a fraction of 1 ℓ in its lowest terms.	(a) 0.7 ℓ (b) $\frac{7}{10}$ ℓ
7	The cost of $2\frac{1}{2}$ kg of rice is £5·50. Find the cost of 500 g.	£ 1·10
8	$\begin{array}{r} 154 \\ -\ ** \\ \hline 67 \end{array}$ Find the missing number.	87
9	A bus travelled a distance of 150 km at 60 km/h. How long did the journey take?	$2\frac{1}{2}$ h
10	Name this triangle by (a) its angles (b) its sides. 60° 60°	(a) acute (b) equilateral
11	9996.8 10 000.0 The readings show the number of km travelled by a car before and after a journey. Find in km the length of the journey.	3.2 km

	W	X	Y	Z
length	7 cm	4 cm	5 cm	8 cm
breadth	$1\frac{1}{2}$ cm	3 cm	2 cm	$1\frac{1}{2}$ cm

The chart shows the length and breadth of 4 rectangles. Which two of the rectangles have the same area?   X   Z

Turn back to page 30 and work for the third time Progress Test 2.

Enter the result and the date on the chart.

39

A

			ANSWER
1	$\frac{1}{2}$ m = (a) ☐ cm	(a)	50 cm
	(b) ☐ mm	(b)	500 mm
2	21 thirds = ☐ whole ones		7
3	50p − ☐ p = 21p		29 p
4	£8 ÷ 10 = ☐ p		80 p
5	Find 0.1 of 10 cm.		1 cm
6	408 ÷ ☐ = 6		68
7	☐ − 99.25 = 0.75		100
8	£1·95 = ☐ TWENTIES + 3 FIVES		9 TWENTIES
9	(8p × 8) + (4p × 9)		£ 1·00
10	£0·78 + £0·46		£ 1·24
11	2.7 km − 1900 m = ☐ m		800 m
12	0.4 m − 0.04 m = ☐ cm		36 cm

B

			ANSWER
1	How many pence have the same value as (a) £0·1	(a)	10 p
	(b) £0·9?	(b)	90 p
2	Find in mℓ $\frac{1}{10}$ of 15 ℓ.		1500 mℓ
3	Two angles of a triangle measure 90° and 55°. Find the measurement of the third angle.		35°
4	Divide the sum of the digits from 1 to 6 inclusive by 3.		7
5	Write the time 35 min before 18.10 in 24-hour clock time.		17.35
6	Subtract $1\frac{3}{8}$ from 6.		$4\frac{5}{8}$
7	Find the difference in g between $\frac{1}{2}$ kg and $\frac{3}{10}$ kg.		200 g
8	How many articles costing 6p each can be bought for 84p?		14
9	$\frac{1}{4}$ ℓ costs 8p. Find the cost of $2\frac{1}{2}$ ℓ.		80 p
10	Change each of these fractions to hundredths. (a) $\frac{1}{20}$ (b) $\frac{7}{20}$	(a) $\frac{5}{100}$ (b) $\frac{35}{100}$	
11	Write the missing numbers in this series. 2, 4, 8, ☐, ☐, 64		16 , 32
12	$\frac{5}{6}$ of a sum of money is £35. Find the whole amount.		£ 42

C

			ANSWER
1	300 g 0.4 kg $\frac{1}{2}$ kg 1.1 kg Find the difference in g between the largest and the smallest of these masses.		800 g
2	Find the total value of these coins.		£ 2·05
3	This clock is 7 min slow. How many minutes is it from the correct time to midnight?		31 min
4	Which of the lines are perpendicular to the line XY?		K M
5	5 metres of cloth cost £3·00. Find the cost of (a) 1 m	(a)	60 p
	(b) 20 cm.	(b)	12 p
6	Through how many right angles does the hour-hand of a clock turn in 24 hours?		8
7	AB is a part of the circumference of a circle 2.8 cm in diameter. Find in mm the length of the line OD.		14 mm
8	Wasim 10 years / James 9 years / Emily ☐ years / Sunil 10 years. The average age of the children is 9 years. How old is Emily?		7 years
9	A tape 20 m long is cut into 100 equal pieces. Find the length in cm of one piece.		20 cm
10	At a sale, shorts were reduced by 12p in the £1. How much was paid for the shorts which cost £10 before the sale?		£ 8·80
11	In a class library there were 158 non-fiction books and 132 fiction books. How many short of 350 books was the total?		60
12	Write the letter of the shape which is (a) a rhombus	(a)	X
	(b) a parallelogram.	(b)	Z

Section 3   Test 10

A

		ANSWER
1	£15·00 ÷ 100	15p
2	1.8 kg − 900 g	900 g
3	47 × 7	329
4	$\frac{1}{2} - \frac{1}{5}$	$\frac{3}{10}$
5	$\frac{3}{10}$ of 1 hour = min	18 min
6	180 mℓ × 100 = ℓ	18 ℓ
7	6.30 p.m. to midnight = h	$5\frac{1}{2}$ h
8	5 FIVES + TENS = £3·65	34 TENS
9	0.35 × 6	2.10
10	0.3 + 0.07 + 3.5	3.87
11	3.05 m − 0.5 m = cm	255 cm
12	£4 − p = £3·11	89p

B

		ANSWER
1	Complete this series. 950, 975, , , 1050	1000, 1025
2	Multiply 2.5 by 6.	15.0
3	How many times can $\frac{1}{12}$ be taken from a whole one?	12
4	The average of 8 numbers is 7. Find the sum of the eight numbers.	56
5	How many cm in $\frac{1}{10}$ of 6.2 m?	62 cm
6	Divide 2 by 5. Write the answer as a decimal fraction.	0.4
7	Find the total distance in km of 350 m, 900 m and $\frac{3}{4}$ km.	2 km
8	What fraction of £3 is 30p?	$\frac{1}{10}$
9	Reduce £6 by £1·73.	£ 4·27
10	Find the cost of 2 ℓ, if 200 mℓ cost 8p.	80'p
11	Write the fraction in its lowest terms which lies midway between $\frac{3}{8}$ and $\frac{5}{8}$.	$\frac{1}{2}$
12	The circumference of a wheel is 50 cm. How many times will it turn in $\frac{1}{2}$ km?	1000

C

		ANSWER
1	How many 75-mℓ bottles can be filled from $7\frac{1}{2}$ ℓ?	100
2	Find the length of a line 10 times the length of the line ST (a) in cm	(a) 55 cm
	(b) in m.	(b) 0.55 m
3	Write the next fraction in this series. $\frac{1}{8}, \frac{1}{4}, \frac{3}{8}, \frac{1}{2},$	$\frac{5}{8}$
4	MARCH — Mon 7 14 21 28 / Tues 1 8 15 22 29 Use this part of a calendar to find	
	(a) the date of the 3rd Monday in March	(a) 21st
	(b) the day of the week upon which 1st April falls.	(b) Friday
5	Biscuits cost 9p for 2. Find the cost of 18.	81p
6	Name this triangle	
	(a) by its angles	(a) obtuse
	(b) by its sides.	(b) scalene
7	Find (a) the area of a rectangle 6 m long and $3\frac{1}{2}$ m wide	(a) 21 m²
	(b) the perimeter of the rectangle.	(b) 19 m
8	In each case give the unit of measurement. The mass of box Y is half the mass of box X. Find in kg and g the total mass of the two boxes.	1 kg 950 g
9	Chloe and Jack shared £5 so that Jack had 50p less than Chloe. How much did Jack have?	£ 2·25
10	The line MN is drawn to a scale of 1 cm to 1 m. Write in m and cm the length represented by the line MN.	4 m 30 cm
11	Of the money Amy receives each week she spends $\frac{3}{5}$ and saves the remainder which is 20p. How much money altogether does she receive each week?	50 p
12	A pack of 20 pins costs 40p. Find the cost of (a) 1 pin	(a) 2p
	(b) 10 packs of pins.	(b) £ 4·00

Section 3　Test 11

A

		ANSWER
1	9000 + ▨ + 7 + 70 = 9777	700
2	3.01 × 100	301
3	4.05 ÷ 9	0.45
4	(7 × 7) = 100 − ▨	51
5	(0.1 of £1) + (0.01 of £1) = ▨ p	11p
6	▨ TWENTIES = £9	45 TWENTIES
7	$1\frac{1}{3} + \frac{5}{6}$	$2\frac{1}{6}$
8	36p + 45p + 19p = £▨	£ 1·00
9	$\frac{7}{8}$ of 72	63
10	1.1 km − 640 m = ▨ m	460 m
11	50 min + 28 min + ▨ min = 2 h	42 min
12	£19 ÷ 5	£ 3·80

B

		ANSWER
1	Subtract 0.01 from 0.1.	0.09
2	How many thousands equal fifty hundreds?	5 thousands
3	Find how many (a) cm (b) mm there are in 0.7 m.	(a) 70 cm
		(b) 700 mm
4	$\frac{1}{2}$ kg costs 20p. Find the cost of (a) 100 g.	(a) 4 p
	(b) 800 g.	(b) 32p
5	By how much is 99p less than 24 FIVES?	21p
6	Multiply £5·09 by 7 and write the answer to the nearest £.	£ 36·00
7	Write as a decimal fraction (a) $\frac{1}{5}$	(a) 0.2
	(b) $\frac{1}{50}$.	(b) 0.02
8	Find the difference between (4.0 + 6.0) and (0.4 + 0.6).	9
9	Change 1050p to £s.	£ 10·50
10	Add 6² and 4².	52
11	Name (a) the sixth month	(a) June
	(b) the ninth month of the year.	(b) September
12	How many pennies are 24 TWOS more than 9 FIVES?	3p

C

		ANSWER
1	Add 8.3 to 5.19 and write the answer to the nearest whole number.	13

2   Bottle X holds twice as much as bottle Y. Write the amount bottle X holds in ℓ and mℓ.　3 ℓ　400 mℓ

3

0.9	0.01	0.25	0.09	0.75

Which two of these fractions when added together equal
(a) a whole one　　　　(a)　0.25　0.75
(b) one tenth?　　　　　(b)　0.01　0.09

4	Find the difference between a half of 18 and one sixth of 30.	4
5	100 pieces of cheese each having a mass of 55 g are packed in a box. The box has a mass of 500 g. Find the total mass of the full box.	6 kg
6	Write the next two fractions in this series. 2, 1, $\frac{1}{2}$, $\frac{1}{4}$, ▨,	$\frac{1}{8}$, $\frac{1}{16}$

7 The mass of some bananas is shown on the dial. Find their cost at 30p per kg.　£ 1·05

8	William scored 51 with 3 darts. He scored 19 and 16 with the first two darts. What was his third score?	16

9

Mon.	150 km
Tues.	150 km
Wed.	100 km
Thurs.	100 km
Fri.	100 km

Mr Gupta travelled these distances in 5 days. What was his average daily journey?　120 km

10 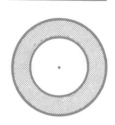 The two circles have the same centre. The inner circle has a diameter of 15 mm. The outer circle has a diameter of 25 mm. Find the width of the shaded part.　5 mm

11  In this right-angled triangle, what is the size in degrees of the angle marked A?　60°

12 $\frac{28}{7} = \frac{36}{x}$　Find the value of x.　9

Section 3 Test 12

A

		ANSWER
1	£1·45 + 86p = £	£ 2·31
2	$\frac{7}{8}$ + = $1\frac{1}{2}$	$\frac{5}{8}$
3	40.5 ÷ 10	4.05
4	$\begin{array}{r}£1·93\\2\overline{)£x}\end{array}$ Find the value of x.	£ 3·86
5	cm × 10 = 1.40 m	14 cm
6	£3 − £ = £0·72	£ 2·28
7	117 min = h min	1 h 57 min
8	0.4 kg − g = 130 g	270 g
9	45 ÷ 9 = 40 ÷	8
10	350 mℓ × 8 = ℓ	2.8 ℓ
11	999 × 3	2997
12	15 km − 10.5 km = m	4500 m

B

		ANSWER
1	Write as a decimal 403 hundredths.	4.03
2	What fraction of 1 hour is 12 minutes?	$\frac{1}{5}$
3	How many TWENTIES are equal in value to £0·8?	4
4	Find the difference between $(\frac{4}{7} + \frac{3}{7})$ and 7.	6
5	Divide the sum of £3·50 and 75p by 5.	85p
6	Write 10 ℓ 250 mℓ to (a) the nearest ℓ (b) the nearest $\frac{1}{2}$ ℓ.	(a) 10 (b) $10\frac{1}{2}$ ℓ
7	Reduce each of these fractions to its lowest terms. (a) $\frac{15}{25}$ (b) $\frac{60}{100}$	(a) $\frac{3}{5}$ (b) $\frac{3}{5}$
8	What must be added to 3 TENS and 6 FIVES to make 90p?	30p
9	0.24 m $\frac{1}{4}$ m 1.0 m 120 cm Subtract the shortest measurement from the longest.	96 cm
10	Find the average of 5, 6, 7, 8 and 9.	7
11	8 strips each measure 65 cm. Find their total length in m.	5.2 m
12	600 mℓ cost 42p. Find the cost of 1 ℓ.	70p

C

		ANSWER
1	How many packets each containing 250 g can be made from 10 kg?	40
2	x y 34.94 Find the difference between the 4 marked x and the 4 marked y.	3.96
3	[diagram: rectangle 2 cm by 10 cm with shaded triangle] Find (a) the area of the shaded triangle (b) the perimeter of the rectangle. Write the unit of measurement in each case.	(a) 10 cm² (b) 24 cm
4	How many pens each costing 60p can be bought for £4·80?	8
5	[coins: 50p, 20p, 10p, 5p] Find the total value of the coins.	£ 3·70
6	[circle diagram with 70° and angles x, y, z] Find the size in degrees of ∠x, ∠y, ∠z.	∠x 110° ∠y 70° ∠z 110°
7	A Dinky caravan is 3350 mm in length and a Comfort caravan is 3.5 m long. By how many mm is the Comfort longer than the Dinky?	150 mm
8	The total length of the sides of an isosceles triangle is 840 mm. The shortest side measures 240 mm. Find the length of each of the other two sides.	300 mm
9	A motorist travelled to Blackpool in $2\frac{1}{2}$ h at an average speed of 64 km/h. What distance did he travel?	160 km
10	60p is made up of an equal number of FIVES and TENS. How many FIVES are there?	4 FIVES
11	The diameter of a 10p coin is 24.5 mm. Ten coins are placed side by side in a straight line. Find the length of the line in cm.	24.5 cm
12	[circle diagram] The circumference of this circle is 22 cm and the radius is 3.5 cm. Find the perimeter of the semicircle.	18 cm

Turn back to page 30 and work for the fourth time Progress Test 2.

Enter the result and the date on the chart.

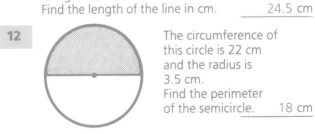

43

CHECK-UP TEST   Number

A

Write in figures.

nine hundred and sixty	960	four thousand and six	4006	one point one nine	1·19
four hundred and eight	408	ten point one	10.1	twenty point nought two	20.02
eight thousand and seventy	8070	three point nought five	3.05		

B

3000 + 500 + ☐ + 9 = 3569	60	7.0 + 0.5 + 0.01 = ☐	7.51
6000 + ☐ + 80 + 1 = 6881	800	10.0 + 0.4 = ☐	10.4
3 + 40 + 9000 = ☐	9043	6.0 + 0.02 = ☐	6.02
(1000 × 4) + (100 × 9) + (10 × 3) = ☐	4930	20.0 + 0.08 = ☐	20.08

C

				Write as a decimal.			
456 = ☐ tens + 6 units	45	tens		1 tenth	0.1	$\frac{9}{10}$	0.9
903 = ☐ tens + 3 units	90	tens		1 hundredth	0.01	$\frac{18}{100}$	0.18
1875 = ☐ tens + 5 units	187	tens		101 tenths	10.1	$\frac{95}{100}$	0.95
5102 = ☐ hundreds + 2 units	51	hundreds		105 hundredths	1.05	$\frac{20}{100}$	0.2
9040 = ☐ hundreds + 4 tens	90	hundreds					

D

Write the value of the figure underlined.

467	60	3751	700	32.14	$\frac{1}{10}$	865.8	$\frac{8}{10}$
8479	8000	2008	8	10.95	$\frac{5}{100}$	40.06	$\frac{6}{100}$
32.5	2	160.2	60	0.56	$\frac{5}{10}$	20.02	$\frac{2}{100}$

E

How many times smaller is

5 than 50	10	96 than 960	10	0.6 than 6.0	10	0.3 than 30	100
7 than 700	100	23 than 2300	100	0.1 than 10.0	100	0.07 than 0.7	10
270 than 2700	10	54 than 5400	100	0.08 than 8.0	100	0.25 than 25?	100

How many times larger is

390 than 39	10	400 than 40	10	8.0 than 0.8	10	50 than 0.5	100
4500 than 45	100	9000 than 90	100	16.0 than 1.6	10	0.4 than 0.04	10
3100 than 31	100	6140 than 614	10	9.0 than 0.09	100	17 than 0.17?	100

F

7 + 8	15	17 + 7	24	11 − 6	5	26 − 9	17
6 + 5	11	8 + 25	33	13 − 8	5	22 − 6	16
9 + 9	18	59 + 6	65	15 − 9	6	43 − 5	38
4 + 7	11	5 + 76	81	11 − 8	3	61 − 4	57
8 + 3	11	46 + 8	54	14 − 7	7	85 − 7	78
9 + 7	16	7 + 89	96	12 − 3	9	93 − 9	84
7 + 5	12	38 + 7	45	17 − 8	9	32 − 8	24
5 + 9	14	4 + 59	63	14 − 9	5	54 − 6	48
4 + 8	12	69 + 5	74	12 − 7	5	72 − 5	67
9 + 4	13	8 + 34	42	14 − 8	6	41 − 3	38
8 + 9	17	77 + 6	83	13 − 6	7	82 − 9	73
6 + 6	12	9 + 68	77	11 − 7	4	95 − 6	89
3 + 8	11	43 + 9	52	13 − 4	9	67 − 9	58
8 + 6	14	6 + 87	93	16 − 7	9	56 − 8	48

G

Find the value of x.

x − 9 = 3	12	14 − x = 5	9	x + 7 = 13	6	8 + x = 14	6
8 + x = 15	7	x − 5 = 8	13	12 − x = 4	8	x − 7 = 9	16
x − 7 = 4	11	9 + x = 15	6	9 + x = 18	9	x + 9 = 17	8
x + 2 = 11	9	x − 8 = 8	16	x − 5 = 7	12		

44

CHECK-UP TEST   Number

A

7 × 7	49	(6 × 9) + 8	62	36 ÷ 9	4	30 ÷ 8	3	rem. 6
8 × 6	48	(4 × 8) + 7	39	49 ÷ 7	7	16 ÷ 9	1	rem. 7
3 × 7	21	(5 × 7) + 6	41	30 ÷ 5	6	20 ÷ 3	6	rem. 2
5 × 9	45	(6 × 3) + 2	20	72 ÷ 8	9	54 ÷ 8	6	rem. 6
7 × 8	56	(1 × 9) + 5	14	24 ÷ 6	4	80 ÷ 9	8	rem. 8
6 × 6	36	(2 × 7) + 6	20	0 ÷ 4	0	63 ÷ 8	7	rem. 7
4 × 5	20	(3 × 9) + 6	33	27 ÷ 9	3	20 ÷ 7	2	rem. 6
9 × 2	18	(7 × 7) + 4	53	42 ÷ 6	7	53 ÷ 9	5	rem. 8
0 × 3	0	(5 × 6) + 3	33	64 ÷ 8	8	21 ÷ 8	2	rem. 5
9 × 9	81	(6 × 8) + 5	53	40 ÷ 5	8	3 ÷ 5	0	rem. 3
8 × 5	40	(0 × 5) + 3	3	18 ÷ 9	2	40 ÷ 7	5	rem. 5
6 × 7	42	(8 × 8) + 7	71	56 ÷ 7	8	19 ÷ 5	3	rem. 4
3 × 8	24	(4 × 9) + 5	41	28 ÷ 4	7	69 ÷ 9	7	rem. 6
9 × 4	36	(8 × 7) + 4	60	32 ÷ 8	4	48 ÷ 7	6	rem. 6
4 × 6	24	(9 × 6) + 5	59	81 ÷ 9	9	16 ÷ 6	2	rem. 4
7 × 9	63	(2 × 8) + 6	22	36 ÷ 6	6	45 ÷ 8	5	rem. 5
4 × 3	12	(4 × 7) + 4	32	35 ÷ 5	7	57 ÷ 6	9	rem. 3
9 × 8	72	(8 × 9) + 8	80	54 ÷ 9	6	31 ÷ 8	3	rem. 7
7 × 4	28	(7 × 6) + 4	46	48 ÷ 6	8	61 ÷ 7	8	rem. 5
3 × 5	15	(3 × 6) + 4	22	63 ÷ 7	9	62 ÷ 9	6	rem. 8

B Find the value of x.

$5 \times x = 40$	8	$x \div 8 = 9$	72	$36 \div x = 9$	4
$x \div 6 = 5$	30	$5 \times x = 45$	9	$4 \times x = 24$	6
$x \times 7 = 42$	6	$x \div 9 = 9$	81	$16 \div x = 4$	4
$27 \div x = 9$	3	$x \times 4 = 32$	8	$x \times 8 = 64$	8
$9 \times x = 63$	7	$21 \div x = 3$	7	$x \div 4 = 7$	28

C

$\frac{1}{2}$ of 18	9	$\frac{1}{4}$ of 28	7	$\frac{3}{4}$ of 20	15	$\frac{2}{5}$ of 45	18
$\frac{1}{3}$ of 21	7	$\frac{1}{5}$ of 40	8	$\frac{5}{6}$ of 54	45	$\frac{4}{7}$ of 35	20
$\frac{1}{6}$ of 36	6	$\frac{1}{8}$ of 32	4	$\frac{7}{8}$ of 48	42	$\frac{7}{9}$ of 63	49
$\frac{1}{9}$ of 45	5	$\frac{1}{10}$ of 100	10	$\frac{3}{10}$ of 70	21	$\frac{9}{10}$ of 80	72

D Find the whole number when

$\frac{1}{3}$ is 8	24	$\frac{1}{5}$ is 6	30	$\frac{5}{6}$ is 30	36	$\frac{4}{5}$ is 16	20
$\frac{1}{6}$ is 7	42	$\frac{1}{8}$ is 9	72	$\frac{7}{8}$ is 21	24	$\frac{2}{7}$ is 12	42
$\frac{1}{9}$ is 4	36	$\frac{1}{10}$ is 12	120	$\frac{4}{9}$ is 36	81	$\frac{7}{10}$ is 49.	70

E

11 × 10	110	130 ÷ 10	13	1.3 × 10	13	4.0 ÷ 10	0.4
100 × 10	1000	800 ÷ 10	80	0.96 × 10	9.6	66.0 ÷ 10	6.6
145 × 10	1450	4620 ÷ 10	462	0.02 × 10	0.2	0.3 ÷ 10	0.03
15 × 100	1500	1900 ÷ 100	19	10.8 × 100	1080	7.0 ÷ 100	0.07
120 × 100	12 000	6500 ÷ 100	65	0.05 × 100	5	19.0 ÷ 100	0.19
104 × 100	10 400	10 000 ÷ 100	100	1.13 × 100	113	403.0 ÷ 100	4.03

F Find the missing numerator or denominator.

$\frac{2}{5} = \frac{4}{10}$	$\frac{3}{4} = \frac{9}{12}$	$\frac{1}{5} = \frac{20}{100}$	$\frac{1}{10} = \frac{10}{100}$	$\frac{50}{100} = \frac{1}{2}$
$\frac{2}{3} = \frac{8}{12}$	$\frac{5}{6} = \frac{10}{12}$	$\frac{3}{5} = \frac{60}{100}$	$\frac{3}{10} = \frac{30}{100}$	$\frac{75}{100} = \frac{3}{4}$
$\frac{5}{8} = \frac{10}{16}$	$\frac{7}{20} = \frac{35}{100}$	$\frac{1}{25} = \frac{4}{100}$	$\frac{7}{10} = \frac{70}{100}$	$\frac{20}{100} = \frac{1}{5}$

CHECK-UP TEST　　Money and Time

A　Write in each box the coins which make up the given amount. Use the least possible number of coins.

32p	20p 10p 2p		54p	50p 2p 2p		65p	50p 10p 5p
80p	50p 20p 10p		67p	50p 10p 5p 2p		18p	10p 5p 2p 1p
26p	20p 5p 1p		71p	50p 20p 1p		59p	50p 5p 2p 2p

B　Find the change from each amount.

Amount	Spent	CHANGE		Amount	Spent	CHANGE		Amount	Spent	CHANGE
50p	24p	26p		90p	81p	9p		£3	£2·13	£0·87
50p	35p	15p		60p	52p	8p		£4	£1·25	£2·75
50p	12p	38p		30p	23p	7p		£4	£2·48	£1·52
50p	37p	13p		45p	41p	4p		£5	£3·09	£1·91
50p	28p	22p		£1	24p	76p		£5	£2·46	£2·54
50p	19p	31p		£1	37p	63p		£5	£1·67	£3·33
50p	23p	27p		£2	£1·69	31p		£5	£2·11	£2·89
50p	16p	34p		£2	£1·06	94p		£5	£0·88	£4·12

C

10 FIVES =	25	TWOS	£7·50 =	15	FIFTIES	£2·55 =	12 TWENTIES, 3 FIVES
6 FIVES =	15	TWOS	£10·00 =	20	FIFTIES	£1·72 =	8 TWENTIES, 6 TWOS
14 FIVES =	7	TENS	£3·80 =	19	TWENTIES	£2·78 =	13 TWENTIES, 9 TWOS
100 FIVES =	50	TENS	£10·00 =	50	TWENTIES	£4·30 =	38 TENS, 1 FIFTY
12 FIVES =	3	TWENTIES	£5·00 =	50	TENS	£3·80 =	7 FIFTIES, 3 TENS
50 TENS =	25	TWENTIES	£7·50 =	75	TENS	£4·25 =	8 FIFTIES, 5 FIVES
45 TENS =	9	FIFTIES	£5·00 =	100	FIVES	£2·90 =	5 FIFTIES, 4 TENS
65 TENS =	13	FIFTIES	£2·20 =	44	FIVES	£1·64 =	3 FIFTIES, 7 TWOS

D

24p + 36p + 50p = £1·10	£1·35 − 60p = £0·75	£2·24 + £3·09 = £5·33
39p + 41p + 22p = £1·02	£2·70 − 85p = £1·85	£4·75 − £2·80 = £1·95
25p + 75p + 9p = £1·09	£4·60 − 99p = £3·61	£1·62 + £1·38 = £3·00
63p + 28p + 12p = £1·03	£2·29 − £0·74 = £1·55	£1·50 − £0·77 = £0·73
82p + 63p + 15p = £1·60	£3·20 − £2·93 = £0·27	£3·87 + £0·45 = £4·32

E　Find the cost of

5 kg at 25p per kg	£1·25	$1\frac{1}{2}$ ℓ at 28p per ℓ	£0·42	5 m at £1·18 per m	£5·90
$3\frac{1}{2}$ kg at 30p per kg	£1·05	3 ℓ at 55p per ℓ	£1·65	75 cm at £1 per m	£0·75
$4\frac{1}{2}$ kg at 20p per $\frac{1}{2}$ kg	£1·80	$2\frac{1}{2}$ ℓ at 22p per ℓ	£0·55	$4\frac{1}{2}$ m at 50p per m	£2·25
2 kg at 50p per 200 g	£5·00	$\frac{1}{2}$ ℓ at 60p per 100 mℓ	£3·00	$1\frac{1}{4}$ m at 20p per $\frac{1}{2}$ m	£0·50
$6\frac{1}{2}$ kg at 60p per kg	£3·90	750 mℓ at 26p per $\frac{1}{2}$ ℓ	£0·39	2 m at 30p per 20 cm.	£3·00

F　Write the times shown on these clocks　(a) in 12-hour clock times using a.m. or p.m.
　　　　　　　　　　　　　　　　　　　　(b) in 24-hour clock times.

(a) 7.37 a.m.

(b) 07.37

morning

(a) 1.24 p.m.

(b) 13.24

afternoon

(a) 12.45 a.m.

(b) 00.45

morning

(a) 10.19 p.m.

(b) 22.19

evening

CHECK-UP TEST Measures and Shapes

A

1 cm	=	10 mm	0.01 m =	1 cm	0.25 m	=	250 mm	$\frac{1}{4}$ m = 25 cm
0.1 cm	=	1 mm	0.25 m =	25 cm	0.75 m	=	750 mm	$\frac{1}{2}$ m = 50 cm
1 m	=	100 cm	0.75 m =	75 cm	1 km	=	1000 m	$\frac{3}{4}$ m = 75 cm
0.1 m	=	10 cm	1 m =	1000 mm	0.5 km	=	500 m	$\frac{1}{2}$ m = 500 mm
0.8 m	=	80 cm	0.5 m =	500 mm	0.75 km	=	750 m	$\frac{3}{4}$ m = 750 mm

B

184 mm	=	18 cm 4 mm	390 mm	=	39 cm	3258 m	=	3 km 258 m
307 mm	=	30 cm 7 mm	412 mm	=	41.2 cm	5106 m	=	5 km 106 m
465 cm	=	4 m 65 cm	800 cm	=	8 m	8200 m	=	8.2 km
1000 cm	=	10 m 0 cm	330 cm	=	3.3 m	6500 m	=	6.5 km
340 cm	=	3 m 40 cm	785 cm	=	7.85 m	7750 m	=	7.75 km

C

3000 g	=	3 kg	5000 mℓ	=	5 ℓ	$\frac{1}{2}$ kg	=	500 g
5280 g	=	5 kg 280 g	2884 mℓ	=	2 ℓ 884 mℓ	$\frac{1}{4}$ kg	=	250 g
8090 g	=	8 kg 90 g	6160 mℓ	=	6 ℓ 160 mℓ	$\frac{3}{4}$ kg	=	750 g
4400 g	=	4.4 kg	7300 mℓ	=	7.3 ℓ	$\frac{1}{2}$ ℓ	=	500 mℓ
7250 g	=	7.25 kg	900 mℓ	=	0.9 ℓ	$\frac{3}{4}$ ℓ	=	750 mℓ

D

240 g +	260 g	= $\frac{1}{2}$ kg	$\frac{1}{2}$ℓ +	92 mℓ	= 592 mℓ	820 g – 0.7 kg	=	120 g
370 g +	130 g	= $\frac{1}{2}$ kg	$\frac{1}{2}$ℓ +	134 mℓ	= 634 mℓ	925 mℓ – 0.8 ℓ	=	125 mℓ
406 g +	94 g	= $\frac{1}{2}$ kg	$\frac{1}{2}$ℓ +	327 mℓ	= 827 mℓ	0.6 kg + 60 g	=	660 g
215 g +	35 g	= $\frac{1}{4}$ kg	$\frac{1}{4}$ℓ +	60 mℓ	= 310 mℓ	0.25 ℓ + 120 mℓ	=	370 mℓ
198 g +	52 g	= $\frac{1}{4}$ kg	$\frac{1}{4}$ℓ +	175 mℓ	= 425 mℓ	0.75 kg + 240 g	=	990 g

E Work across the page.
Write to the

nearest whole number	$19\frac{3}{4}$	20	$10\frac{1}{3}$	10	14.4	14	11.5 12
nearest hundred	308	300	953	1000	1326	1300	2950 3000
nearest £1	£17·09	£17	£4·83	£5	£32·50	£33	£129·28 £129
nearest cm	7 cm 2 mm	7 cm	109 mm	11 cm	39.6 cm		40 cm
nearest m	8 m 51 cm	9 m	730 cm	7 m	15.3 m		15 m
nearest km	$12\frac{1}{4}$ km	12 km	18 km 900 m	19 km	78.5 km		79 km
nearest kg	4 kg 300 g	4 kg	9 kg 550 g	10 kg	99.25 kg		99 kg
nearest $\frac{1}{2}$ kg	6 kg 200 g	6 kg	12 kg 380 g	$12\frac{1}{2}$ kg	5 kg 600 g		$5\frac{1}{2}$ kg
nearest ℓ	5 ℓ 400 mℓ	5 ℓ	9 ℓ 600 mℓ	10 ℓ	3.7 ℓ		4 ℓ

F

Write the letter of the shape which is

a right-angled triangle	E	a rhombus	G	an obtuse-angled triangle	B
a rectangle	D	a parallelogram	A	an isosceles triangle	F

G How many degrees are there in each of the angles marked x, y and z ?

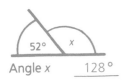

Angle x   128°

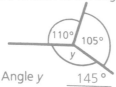

Angle y   145°

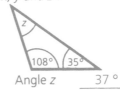

Angle z   37°

Angle x   125°
Angle y   55°

47

Full list of the *Schofield & Sims Mental Arithmetic* books

Pupil books

Mental Arithmetic Introductory Book	ISBN 978 07217 0798 3
Mental Arithmetic Book 1	ISBN 978 07217 0799 0
Mental Arithmetic Book 2	ISBN 978 07217 0800 3
Mental Arithmetic Book 3	ISBN 978 07217 0801 0
Mental Arithmetic Book 4	ISBN 978 07217 0802 7
Mental Arithmetic Book 5	ISBN 978 07217 0803 4
Mental Arithmetic Book 6	ISBN 978 07217 0804 1

Answers

Mental Arithmetic Introductory Book Answers	ISBN 978 07217 0853 9
Mental Arithmetic Book 1 Answers	ISBN 978 07217 0805 8
Mental Arithmetic Book 2 Answers	ISBN 978 07217 0806 5
Mental Arithmetic Book 3 Answers	ISBN 978 07217 0807 2
Mental Arithmetic Book 4 Answers	ISBN 978 07217 0808 9
Mental Arithmetic Book 5 Answers	ISBN 978 07217 0809 6
Mental Arithmetic Book 6 Answers	ISBN 978 07217 0810 2

Related materials

For information about the **I can do** teaching method, which you may use with *Schofield and Sims Mental Arithmetic*, watch the film **'I can do maths' in practice** online at **www.schofieldandsims.co.uk/icando/** and order the

I can do maths Teacher's Guide	ISBN 978 07217 1115 7

For A3 Desk Mats with maths facts on one side and English facts on the other – and ample space for writing pupils' individual targets, order the

I can do Desk Mat (Class set)	Order no. 5060137710000

All available from

Schofield & Sims
Dogley Mill
Fenay Bridge
Huddersfield HD8 0NQ

Web: www.schofieldandsims.co.uk
Tel: 01484 607080
Fax: 01484 606815
E-mail: sales@schofieldandsims.co.uk